D1218209

CHIVA-SOM
NATURAL WAY TO HEALTHY EATING AND LIVING

CHIVA-SOM NATURAL WAY TO HEALTHY EATING AND LIVING

ACKNOWLEDGEMENTS

The Chiva-Som team:

Joy Menzies, General Manager

Claire Branch, Spa Manager

Kuttiya Nimcean, Senior Sous Chef

Buathon Thienarrom, Medical Manager

Sally Oldham, Fitness Manager

Special thanks to:

Naphalai Areesorn, Ana Maria Tavares,

Andrew Jacka, Hunter Reynolds, Lalana Santos

Published by

The Post Publishing Public Company Limited

Printed by Allied Printers

Address: Bangkok Post Building,

136 Na Ranong Road,

Klong Toey, Bangkok 10110, Thailand

Tel: (66 2) 240-3700

Fax: (66 2) 240-3698

Email: allied@bangkokpost.co.th

Project Editor: Prapai Kraisornkovit

Publishing Manager: Wisanu Sasi-smit

Editor: Naphalai Areesorn

Writer: Ken Barrett

Designers: Busarin Srisarakham, Pakpen Siri

Food Photographers: Robert McLeod,

Anusorn Sakseree

Food Stylists: Andrew Jacka, Teera Taithong,

Suwit Manee Na Singha

ISBN 974 85403 2 4

CON

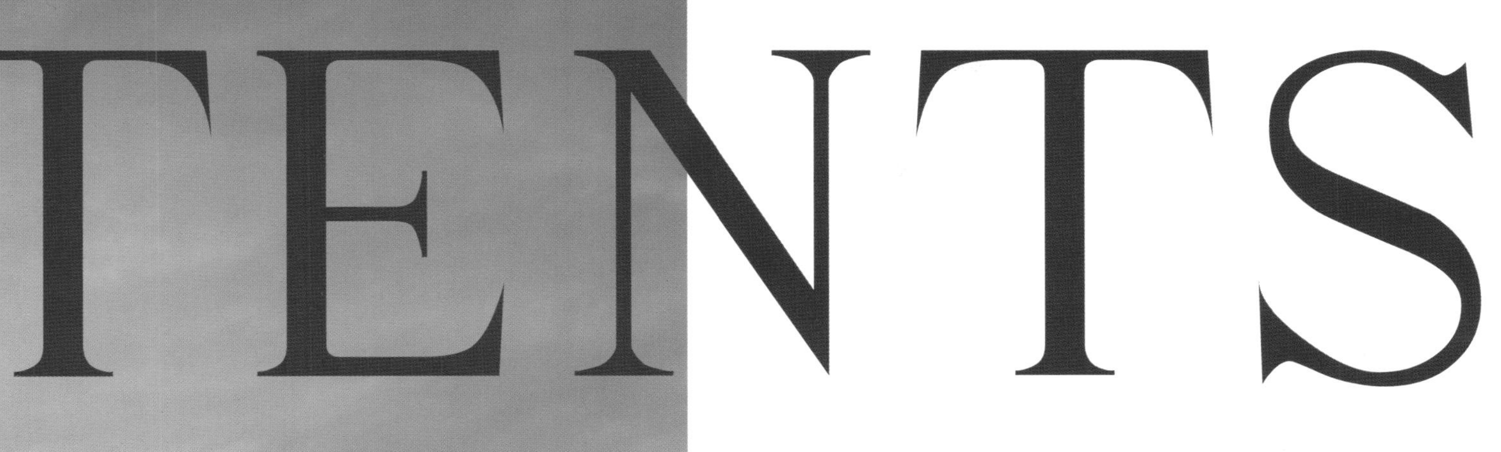
TENTS

CHIVA-SOM NATURAL WAY TO HEALTHY EATING AND LIVING

The ancients understood that if we achieved harmony within ourselves, we would be at peace with the world. Of course, our world has changed in ways that not even the wisest philosopher of old could have foreseen, but the beliefs and principles still hold true. We are only just beginning to realise this.

In recent years, there has been an enormous awakening of interest in traditional medicines and herbal treatments, in meditation, and in the ways in which our minds and bodies work in harmony with the universe. For some it has become a quest for inner peace in a society that all too often treats the individual as a mere component. For others it is the advent of a spirituality that they may not have realised existed within them. Perhaps, after all, the ancients really did hold the keys to the truth.

Alongside this fascination with a world that was a far more tranquil and less populated place, we of course have the enormous advantages that modern civilisation brings. We know far more about the mechanics of our bodies, and how this in turn can affect the workings of our minds. We know how to prevent ailments before they can take hold of us, and we can cure diseases. We have modern technology to help us, and as this is evolving in parallel to our understanding of modern medicine and the health sciences, it seems certain that future generations will live longer and better.

This blending of the old world and the new has been of particular interest to us at Chiva-Som. We are not simply a vacation resort with a spa, neither are we just a luxurious medical centre. We believe that complete physical, mental and spiritual health can be achieved by the individual when he or she applies certain principles and techniques, and our whole philosophy is built around this. This book therefore is not about us. It is about you.

At Chiva-Som, the accent is always on the positive aspects of health prevention rather than cure, innovation rather than accepted practice, the application of wisdom rather than the passive acceptance of aging. We have on our staff health consultants and fitness trainers who have studied under masters, learning the newer as well as the established techniques.

We have too a team of chefs who have developed a cuisine that perfectly compliments, and in fact enhances, this approach to health and wellbeing. In addition, our specialist consultants, often completely unique in their own field, visit us regularly to share their own experiences and expertise with our guests.

Chiva-Som Natural Way to Healthy Eating and Living is therefore a distillation of all that we do and know at Chiva-Som, in which you will participate during your stay with us. At the end of your stay, we encourage you to continue with them in your own home, in your own time. This book is therefore a logical extension of our first, *The Art of Healthy Eating and Living with Chiva-Som.* It explains the roots of our physical makeup and how these affect our mental and consequently our spiritual health.

By taking charge of our physical side we can also take charge of our destiny. The old civilisations understood this, creating their own baths, treatments, therapies and healing centres out of their natural surroundings. They understood the energy forces of the body, and how these are part of a greater whole. *Chiva-Som Natural Way to Healthy Eating and Living* continually stresses the words "harmony" and "tranquillity", because although these are ultimately inner qualities, they begin with the environment that we each create for ourselves. Anyone who enters Chiva-Som for the first time will be overwhelmed by the sense of peace that permeates our beach-side health resort. The name itself translates as "Haven of Life", and our aims are threefold: to achieve immediate, tangible benefits, to learn how to extend these into a lifestyle, and to have fun.

We are the first destination spa in Asia, created by those who understand the mainsprings of human happiness. Having been voted the world's top health spa resort by the readership of *Conde Nast Traveller* as well as other international publications, we feel a tremendous sense of accomplishment and responsibility.

An old saying has it that "we are what we eat", and the greater part of this book is devoted to our recipe section. Unless we eat properly, true health and harmony will elude us. Each of the recipes included has been developed by our own chefs, and is designed to ensure our bodies have the right input of fuel and run at their most efficient level. Every one of the recipes is easy enough to prepare in your own home, and uses ingredients that are not difficult to source.

It is our sincere belief that healthy eating does not mean boring eating. A meal of natural, low-calorie, nutritious food can be a gourmet experience. At Chiva-Som, many of the fruits and vegetables are grown in our organic garden, and we encourage you to seek out ingredients that are free of pesticides and other chemicals. But other than this, there is nothing special that is needed. Further, this is not vegetarian food. We use fresh fish, free-range poultry, and lean red meat. Our chefs' objective is to present the clean flavours of the individual ingredients, rather than have them smothered with rich, palate-clogging sauces and additives. The food is therefore alive with natural colours and textures.

You can make it your own personal philosophy to be positive about your physical and mental health by taking responsibility for the quality of your life. It is with pleasure therefore that we introduce you to *Chiva-Som Natural Way to Healthy Eating and Living.* May it provide a very practical guide to your complete happiness and wellbeing

Rejuvenating

No matter how far back into history we travel, we find use being made of the restorative powers of water. Hot, cold, bubbling, muddy, mineral-rich – the ancients seem to have understood the properties of all forms of water and how they react with the body. Public baths dating back 4,500 years have been found during excavations in the Indus Valley, in what is now Pakistan. The Babylonians, Egyptians and Greeks also took to the waters of public baths for rejuvenation. The Roman Empire spread the idea of the spa throughout much of the known world, with Roman spa towns such as Bath in England and Aquincum in Hungary still thriving today.

In fact the word "spa" is the acronym of Emperor Nero's famous statement in support of the great Roman bath projects: Sanitas per aquas, or health through water. During the 17th and 18th centuries, physicians in Europe began extolling the benefits of spa water, and by the 1800s new spa towns like Baden-Baden in Germany and Vichy in France were being built for the aristocratic and the rich. Spas caught on in the United States as well, being built around natural phenomena such as the hot springs at Arkansas and the mud baths of Calistoga, California.

Today's spa draws on practices that have evolved over many millennia, a legacy of long-gone cultures passed on down to us. As a form of knowledge it is a wonderful gift. From India and Japan come massage techniques that evolved with the rise of Buddhism. The Romans understood steam treatments and massage. The mediaeval Turks created the five stages of today's spa bath experience: dry heat, moist heat, massage, cold and then rest. The Swedes and the Finns contributed the practice of sweating in a hot sauna and then plunging into icy-cold water. The English and Europeans drank the mineral waters for their inner cleansing effects. As spas become more accessible to everyone, so the benefits of these ancient therapies will enrich the lives of us all.

1 powers of spas

WELLNESS WITH WATER: THE USE OF HYDROTHERAPY

Water can be used on or in the body to enhance health and treat a variety of health problems. For example, while fasting it is important to drink enough water to help cleanse the body of wastes and toxins. Swimming exercises muscles and relieves tension. A steam bath or sauna invigorates the body and induces sweating to flush out impurities, which is why it is an effective way of combatting head colds. Cold baths and showers are energising and stimulating, and alternating hot and cold water enhances circulation and organ functioning.

These treatments are used for the prevention of diseases linked to cardiovascular problems and fatigue. Absorption of minerals and trace elements through the skin restores the balance within the cells. Drainage of toxins by means of osmosis and stimulation of the lymph circulation have a lasting reactivating effect. Blood in the outer vessels is stimulated and circulates faster, and as this means a larger supply of arterial blood, the body benefits from better oxygenation.

At Chiva-Som we recommend heat treatments prior to hydrotherapy to warm the muscles and aid the relaxation process. The sauna is set at a temperature of 78 degrees C, and the steam at 48 degrees C. The heat increases blood circulation, and perspiration helps cleanse the body and the muscles and body relax. Blood pressure is temporarily lowered and the body and muscles relax. After this, the cool plunge contracts the peripheral vessels, driving the blood deeper. The respiratory rate increases, as does the basal metabolic rate, and the cutaneous elastic fibres contract. There is an increased tone and energy in the muscles, and a general feeling of exhilaration.

Also available is underwater massage in a hydrotherapy bath consisting of 130 water jets; this stimulates circulation, tones muscle tissue and provides relaxation throughout the body. Body blitz is a technique in which a high-pressure water jet directed at your body works on lymph drainage and stimulates circulation in specific problem areas to eliminate cellulite and smooth skin tissue. Blood and lymphatic circulation is increased, and the breakdown of fat is stimulated. As with other forms of hydrotherapy, the water helps to drain away toxins.

The oldest records describing what we now call 'hydrotherapy' can be found in 6,000-year-old Sanskrit writings. Hydrotherapy is therapy with water in any of its forms; ice-cold water, hot water, steam, freshwater, or water imbued with special minerals. Balneo therapy indicates a treatment with tap water, thalasso therapy uses sea water, and thermal therapy is water treatment using hot springs.

To de-stress, there is a floatation room at Chiva-Som, essentially a shell enclosing a 10-inch deep saline solution maintained at body temperature. You experience a sensation of floating as if one is back in the protective womb, which induces an extremely deep state of mental relaxation, helping to eliminate stress and tension.

At home, although they may seem routine, baths and showers are healing and health-promoting activities. Adding certain natural ingredients to bathwater can boost its detoxifying power and relaxation potential. A blend of four drops of juniper, to enhance blood flow, two drops of grapefruit, two drops of rosemary, and one teaspoon of vegetable oil added to a bathful of water is one suggestion.

Another bath recipe that can restore natural body salts and cleanse the body combines a half-cup each of sea salt and Epsom salts, plus one-third cup of dried kelp or dulse seaweed in a blender to form a powder. Add this mixture to your bathwater, or use it as a skin scrub.

A sitz bath is a European tradition that immerses the pelvis and lower abdomen in hot or cold water or alternating hot and cold. A hot sitz bath is recommended for uterine cramps, painful ovaries or testicles, prostate infections and hemorrhoids, while a brief cold sitz bath is good for easing inflammation, constipation, vaginal discharge and impotence.

Dizziness, nausea, insomnia, shivering, cold feet, foot and leg cramps, sore throats, colds and flu respond to a hot foot bath, but be sure to wrap your upper body in a blanket to avoid chills and promote sweating. Alternating hot and cold foot baths can treat swollen ankles, foot infections and even toothache. A hand bath, simply dipping your hand into hot water, relieves hand cramps. Immersing the hand in cold water is helpful for stopping nosebleeds and treating sunstroke.

Chamomile, lavender and linden flowers create a calming bath. Essential oils such as lavender, rose, clary sage, ylang ylang, and patchouli relieve stress, headaches, muscle tension and symptoms of premenstrual syndrome. Epsom salts contain magnesium sulphate, which relaxes muscles and calms the nervous system.

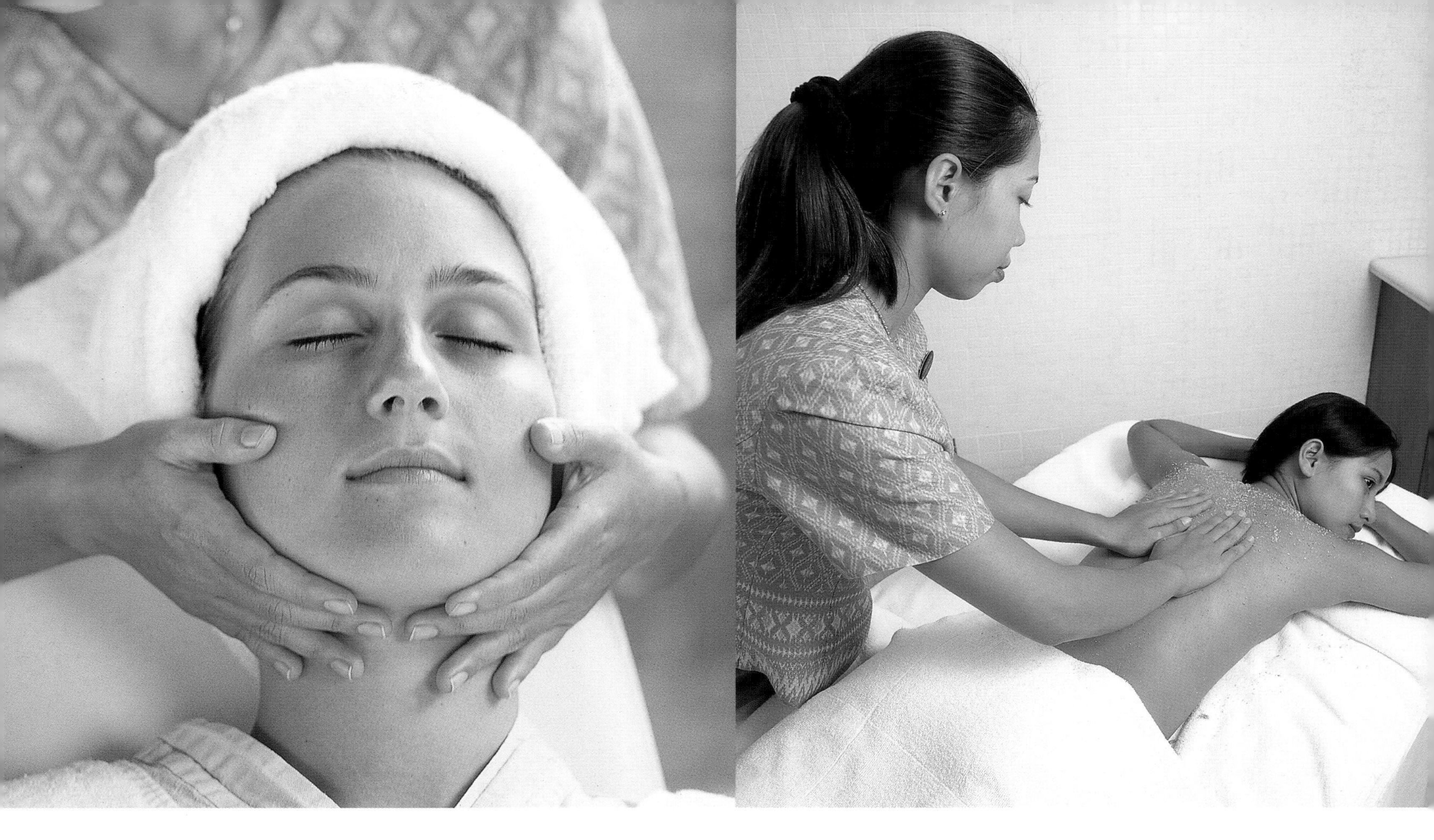

MASSAGE: THE NATURAL THERAPY

Massage is, in its simplest form, an instinctive therapy. The first thing we do when we feel pain anywhere in our bodies is to rub and knead the painful area. Massage therapy was known to the ancient Chinese and Japanese, the Greeks, Romans and Egyptians, and virtually every civilisation since.

Oddly, however, during the 20th century we began to forget about it. The development of drugs and advanced medical procedures led us to believe that swallowing a pill or visiting a doctor could solve most of our problems. Only recently have we begun to realise that often this is simply treating the symptom rather than the cause, and that there can be unwanted side effects, physical or emotional. So now we are beginning to think preventively, and to see the worth of natural approaches. Massage therapy has made a big come-back.

Massage therapy is based on the fact that the soft tissues – muscles, tendons, ligaments and fascia – respond to touch. Pain is usually myofascial, or soft-tissue, in origin. There are also sensitive points in the muscles that radiate or refer pain to various parts of the body. These are known as trigger points. Our muscles move our joints, they stabilise the workings and balance of our body, and they provide a protective shield for the delicate internal organs. So it is easy to see how pain or stress in a muscle can be transmitted through the body.

For example, most headaches originate in the muscles of the neck. Much of the pain of such conditions as angina comes from the hypercontraction of the chest muscles; while abdominal and pelvic pain is frequently caused by trigger points in the local muscles. Clearly, a skilled and knowledgeable masseur has great potential for treating and preventing pain.

Traditional Chinese medicine, now gaining a huge following in the West, uses charts dating back thousands of years that illustrate the points on the body, hands and feet which correspond to energy channels and trigger points. Today's reflexology treatments are based on this belief that there are places on the feet and hands that correspond to internal organs and joints, and that manipulating them can have direct effects on corresponding parts of the body.

Shiatsu evolved in Japan, and is a system based on the body's energy meridians. Shiatsu massage is normally done fully-clothed and involves pressing points on the body, stretching and opening the energy meridians. The technique is related to acupuncture, which is a form of anaesthesia and therapy developed in China.

Traditional Thai massage has its origins in ancient India before even the time of the Buddha, and was formerly administered only in temple grounds by masters versed in healing. By force on pressure points, muscles and ligaments, stretching and bending and manipulations, the spine is elongated and relieved of tension, joints are stretched and the whole body decompressed.

Swedish massage is a collection of techniques designed to relax the muscles by applying pressure to them against deeper muscles and bones, and rubbing in the same direction as the flow of blood returning to the heart. The lymph system and veins both rely on muscle action, rather than heart pump pressure, to operate. Friction on the skin is reduced by oil. This technique can make you feel especially good, as it relaxes the nervous system.

From the massage techniques of old have evolved many of the modern therapies we use today. Trigger point and myotherapy treatments are pain-relief techniques to alleviate muscle spasms and cramping. The therapist locates and deactivates the trigger points, the areas where the muscles have been bruised or tense, sending signals or spasms to other parts of the body. Often ice or another cooling agent is used to reduce nervous system response, making the area easier and more comfortable to work.

Polarity therapy is a holistic approach based on the fact that energy fields exist everywhere in nature, and that the flow and balance of this energy in the human body is the underlying foundation of health. Stress, tension, pain, negative emotions and the immediate environment are among the many factors that can contribute to the restriction of this energy flow in the human body. Therapists use four methods: bodywork, diet, exercise and self-awareness.

Myofascial therapy is used to evaluate and treat restrictions in the muscles and non-contractile supportive connective tissues, or fascia, by the application of gentle traction, pressures and positioning. Fascia is a complex supportive web throughout the entire body, affecting the musculo-skeletal, nervous and organ systems as it surrounds groups of muscle fibres and entire muscle groups and organs. Muscle tissues can become shortened if they are improperly used, and layers of fascia can stick together.

Myofascial release techniques are therefore used to coax muscles in spasm to relax, and break adhesions in the fascia. Our body responds by releasing tension that has been stored in the fascia, thus allowing more functional flexibility and mobility of the muscles, fascia and associated structures.

Craniosacral therapy can be considered to be a type of myofascial release. It is especially suited to addressing tensions in the craniosacral system, or the membranes that contain the cerebrospinal fluid within the head and spinal column, as well as the head and face bones to which these membranes are attached.

Reiki was developed in Japan a century and a half ago, and is a gentle hands-on healing technique to reduce stress, relieve pain and facilitate healing. This is another technique based on the same energy principles as acupuncture, tai chi chuan and chi kung. But reiki is neither invasive, as is acupuncture, nor does it require physical agility and effort to gain benefits, as do tai chi and chi kung.

There are many other forms of massage-related therapy. Hakomi uses special states of consciousness, with body-mind awareness and touch used to explore the body as a deep source of information, empowering the subject to change and master his or her attitudes. Jin shin do, which translates as "the way of the compassionate spirit", is derived from acupressure and involves applying gentle fingertip pressure to 30 specific points along the body to release, smooth and balance vital chi energy.

Neuromuscular therapy uses advanced concepts in pressure therapy to break the stress-tension-pain cycle. Many of these massage therapies are practised at Chiva-Som, and are increasingly easy to find elsewhere, as the number of tutors and practitioners grows to meet the demand.

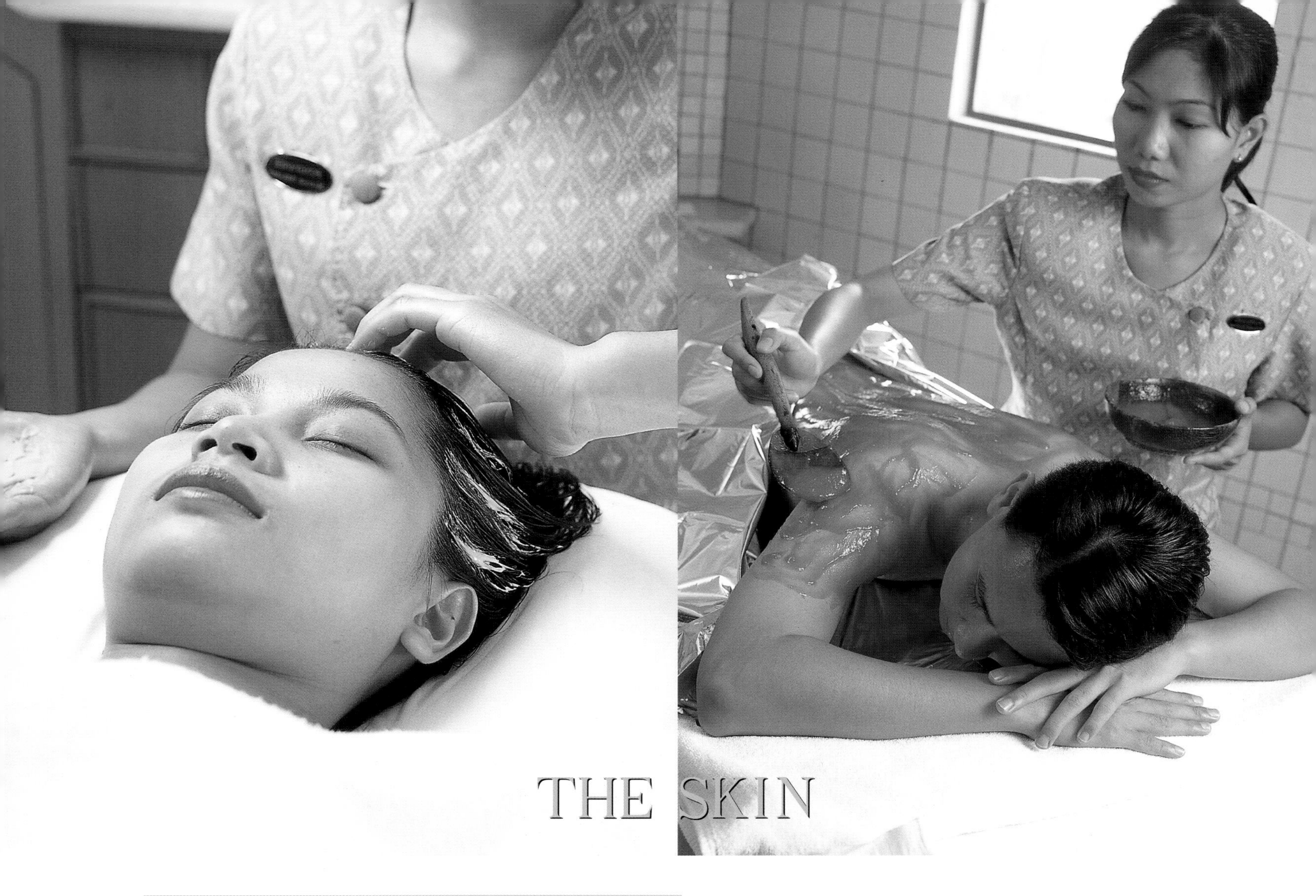

THE SKIN

The skin is the body's largest organ. It flushes toxins outwards by way of perspiration and absorbs nutrients. It produces vitamin D from natural sunshine. It breathes, absorbing oxygen while exhaling carbon dioxide. Thousands of sweat glands expel at least one pound of waste daily, regulate the temperature of our body, and help cleanse the blood and free the system from poisons. Yet, not unnaturally, this vital part of our health and appearance is subject to a huge amount of wear and tear. Exposure to harsh climatic conditions and pollution, use of detergents and coarse soaps, a poor diet, consumption of alcohol, smoking or proximity to tobacco smoke, substance abuse, and a lack of exercise—all can cause immense stress to our skin. As a result, the skin ages, making it less supple and efficient.

The skin is layered. Uppermost is the epidermis, the face that we present to the world. Immediately under this is the dermis, a much more dense layer that consists of pigment – producing cells, sebaceous glands, sweat glands, hair follicles and – most important when it comes to ageing – fibroblasts. Fibroblasts are cells that produce the collagen and elastin fibres that give our skin its strength and resilience. As our skin suffers from the daily stress, and as we get older, its various processes start to slow down. There is reduced oil secretion so the skin tends to become dry, and reduced activity within the cells so it can look dull and lifeless. Fibres and muscles become weak. What we see in the mirror begins to depress us, adding another aspect to the downward curve.

Keeping the muscles of the face strong and supple is something that most of us seldom think about. In fact, many of the facial muscles are underused, and by regular exercise we can not only look our best but also gradually reverse the signs of ageing. The muscles of the face differ from those of the body in that they are attached directly to the skin that covers them. This means that when the facial muscles sag, the skin attached to them sags too. The slackening of the facial muscles is one of the main causes of the sagging and drooping that most of us eventually experience, leading to bags under the eyes, loose folds of skin on the upper eyelids, jowls, turkey-necks, and other signs of advancing years. We actually have an amazing muscle structure under the skin: taking good care of it is as important as exercising the rest of the body.

By following a facial workout, you will feel a definite improvement in your muscle tone in just a few weeks. If you reach an advanced level, you will not only feel the improvement, you will also see your face gradually lifting. Folds on the upper eyelids will decrease, the corners of your mouth will become firmer, and any lines on your upper lip will be reduced. Your neck and jaw line will become firmer and any jowls will lessen and eventually disappear.

Skin brushing is a technique that stimulates the circulation, helping to pump the blood down through the veins and up through the arteries, feeding those organs of the body that lie near the surface. It also stimulates the lymph and adrenal glands. It has a powerful rejuvenating effect on the nervous system because of the hundreds of nerve endings in the skin. Dead skin cells are removed along with other impurities, keeping the pores open and unclogged. Any treatments that are applied to the skin afterwards are more easily absorbed.

Proper care of our lymphatic system will help us beat all kinds of ailments and leave us looking and feeling good. This is a secondary circulatory system to that of blood. Present in the vessels is a fluid called lymph containing the disease-fighting white blood cells, lymphocytes. Some lymphocytes make antibodies to neutralise foreign organisms, while others attach themselves to the organism directly. Lymph nodes or glands are located throughout the system to act as infection filters. The main nodes are situated in the groin, under the arms, the back of the knees, and the crease of the elbows and in the neck.

All you need is a natural bristle brush with a long, wooden, detachable handle. Brushes made from Mexican tapico fibres are the best – the bristles feel stiff to begin with but they soften with use. As skin brushing involves the use of a dry brush on dry skin, it is important to take care of the brush by washing it out once a week with warm water and natural soap. Rinse well and dry thoroughly.

To begin the skin brushing, make sure your skin is dry. Start with the soles of your feet and brush upwards in the direction of your heart. Brush vigorously up the legs and over the thighs, working towards the groin where the lymph nodes lie. Use a circular clockwise movement over the abdomen. Do this about 10 times. Brush your palms and the backs of your hands, then move up the arms to your shoulders. Use downward strokes on your neck and throat, and over your chest.

To stimulate the lymph nodes under your arms you need to create a pumping action. Lodge the thumb under your shoulder bone and with all your fingers grip your chest muscle, making sure the fingertips get right into the armpit. Squeeze and then release this area about 15 times on each side. Attach the handle to the brush so that you can brush across the top of your shoulders and upper back, then up over the buttocks and lower back.

This should take you about five minutes daily. First thing in the morning is the best time to perform the routine, but should you need to brush twice a day, don't brush too close to bedtime or you will be unable to sleep. Brush every day for three months then reduce it to two or three times a week, changing the days each week. After skin brushing you should remove the dead skin cells by showering – start with a hot shower and finish with a cold one.

AROMATHERAPY: THE SOOTHING EFFECTS OF FRAGRANCE

Aromatherapy is the use of fragrant substances for health and beauty treatment. It is often combined with massage since oils can be used to carry fragrances while also allowing more pressure to be applied to muscles. Again, this is a very ancient practice, although much of the history of fragrance is now lost to us. Primitive perfumery probably began with the burning of gums and resins for incense, and eventually richly scented plants were blended with animal and vegetable oils to anoint the body for ceremony and pleasure. The fatty oils of olive and sesame combined with fragrant plants were amongst the first ventures into fragrances.

During the time of the Egyptian pharaoh Khufu, builder of the Great Pyramid (circa 2700 BC), papyrus manuscripts recorded the use of fragrant herbs, choice oils, perfumes and temple incense, and told of healing lotions made of fragrant resins. In ancient Greece, where the word "aromatic" originates, athletes were anointed with scented oils before competing. *The Chinese Yellow Emperor Book of Internal Medicine,* written around 2697 BC, explains various uses of aromatic herbs.

Due to the natural phytochemicals produced by the plants, essential oils can have many different effects on the body, mind and spirit. Essential oils can be sedative or stimulating. During an aromatherapy bath or massage, the aromas are perceived by the nerve endings in the nose, and signals are passed to the limbic system in the brain. One of the functions of the limbic system is to regulate the pituitary gland, which controls hormone release throughout the body. Additionally, the essential oils' molecules are absorbed through the skin, and then dissolve in the natural body fats and fluids. This allows them to flow around the body, to relax or stimulate, detoxify and regenerate.

Aromatherapists adopt a holistic approach, gathering the information necessary to select the appropriate essential oils for maximum therapeutic benefit. Pure, organic oils are blended into the massage oil, to create a unique mix for the individual's specific needs. This blend will often vary with each visit, depending on how the subject feels, and what the response has been each time.

These oxidising agents have a big impact on the way we look and feel. They come in various forms and are simply the waste products of ordinary metabolic processes such as breathing. Some are even beneficial. Most however are destructive: air pollutants, cigarette smoke and pesticides, for example. The most notorious are the so-called oxygen-free radicals. These have lost one of the electrons that keep them chemically stable. In their frantic search for another one, they will take it from anywhere, destroying healthy cells in their path. Oxygen-free radicals attack DNA, the genetic material of our body cells, and are a major cause of aging. Look what happens to an apple when it oxidises: it turns black.

There are foods that have a high concentration of antioxidants and strong antioxidant activity, including avocado, carrot, cumin, oats, citrus fruits, sesame seeds, peppermint and watermelon. Olive oil, when rubbed into human cell membranes, makes them more stable and helps retard the aging process by keeping the cells alive for longer.

Vitamins C and E are important antioxidants. Vitamin C is necessary for the body's immune response to infections and in wound healing, and is essential for maintaining the strength of blood capillaries and for the formation of collagen. In fact, collagen degeneration can be a sign of vitamin C deficiency – when the elasticity of collagen collapses, skin can age very quickly.

Vitamin E is the vitamin that reduces scarring following an accident or surgery. It too is known to prolong cell life, improve skin quality, and hasten healing. If you bruise easily or have very dry skin, vitamin E can make a real difference. Fruits and vegetables that are rich sources of vitamins C and E will benefit the skin if they are taken in the diet and also if they are applied to the skin topically.

As such, fruit and herbal wraps can benefit the skin and at Chiva-Som, they form an important part of our range of treatments. Some of them are rooted in antiquity, others have been developed by our own specialists. Some can be used in your own home, or adapted for use.

One of the most popular is the Thai Fruit Wrap, which is suited to all skins, especially dry or sensitive skin. A body rub is performed using a blend of Thai herbs and flowers, followed by an application of fresh papaya, pineapple and aloe vera. The papaya provides deep moisturising and is a rich source of vitamin A. Pineapple is a plentiful source of vitamin C, while aloe vera is calming and moisturising. The body is then wrapped in plastic sheeting to generate its own heat that will allow the oils to penetrate into the upper layers of the skin. A scalp massage is done while this takes place. Finally, your body is moisturised.

A development of this is the Chiva-Som Experience, a blissful treatment that lasts for 115 minutes and is a combination of fruit wrap, spa bath and an aromatherapy massage. First the body is rubbed with a blend of Thai herbs and flowers. Then comes the spa bath, with restorative essential bath oils and bubble action to massage. Following this, a blend of fresh papaya, pineapple and aloe vera is rubbed into your body, which is then completely wrapped to allow the skin to absorb the nutrients. At the same time your scalp is massaged with oils and scalp mud. The experience concludes with massage using restorative oils.

Another treatment you can enjoy at home is the Bath of Chiva, a relaxing flower bath with warm water and 20 litres of milk, honey, chamomile flowers and rose petals. To obtain real tranquillity, you set the scene with candlelight. The milk is rich in vitamin A to nourish, condition and moisturise the skin. Honey is soothing and softening. Chamomile flowers add their soothing aromatic power, while the rose petals are a touch of visual pleasure.

Then there is the Aloe and Cucumber Wrap, perfect for those who have spent too long in the sun, and for especially sensitive skins. The cucumber is cooling and mildly astringent. Aloe vera is calming, moisturising and healing. The wrap is applied to the back of the body, which is then covered in banana leaves. During this time a foot massage takes place. After 15 minutes the wrap is applied to the front of the body, during which time a scalp massage is performed. The skin is left feeling cool, toned and refreshed.

CREATE YOUR OWN SPA

During our stressful lives we need to take some time out to pamper ourselves. Even if you do not have time to visit exotic spas you can create a functional spa in your own home, using easily accessible natural ingredients. The most indulgent of treatments created using natural produce help us to get back in touch with nature. All you need to do is take a little time to yourself and relax. It is important that you set the scene, for if you create the right environment this will allow you to relax completely.

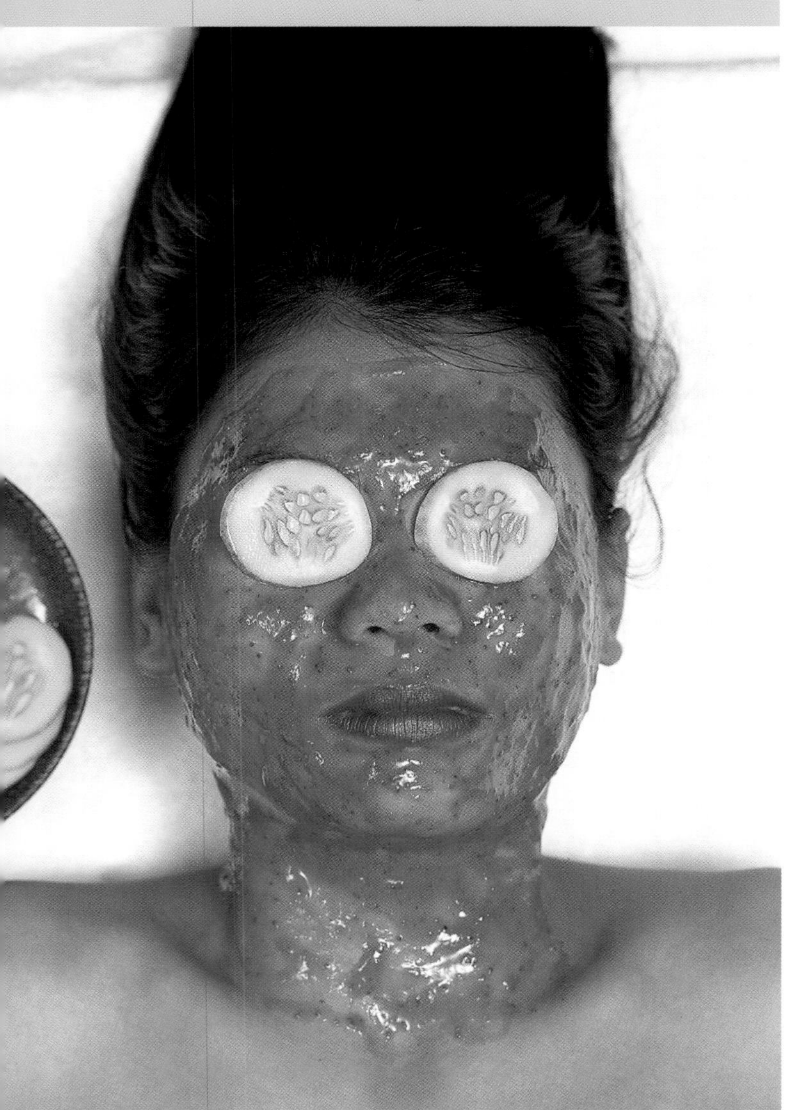

For a comfortable and luxurious atmosphere, warmth and lighting are both very important factors. Switch on the central heating, or turn down the air conditioning if you live in a hot climate, close the curtains, dim the lights and light a few candles. To stimulate your senses, burn essential oils in the rooms you will use. Try oils that help to relax, like lavender, geranium, ylang ylang or chamomile. Inhaling essential oils helps relieve depression and mental fatigue, and relieves anxiety.

Make sure you have plenty of large clean towels and a warm dressing gown, and keep them in the airing cupboard or on the radiator so they feel warm and cosy. Play your favourite CDs to help switch off your mind, and treat yourself to your favourite magazine or a good novel.

NATURAL HAIR AND SKIN CARE

Although there are a huge number of spa beauty preparations on the market, you can devise your own with the kind of ingredients that are easily available in your kitchen or from local stores. Experiment a little and find out what you like best.

Hair conditioning

It may sound like an unpleasant idea but applying raw egg to your hair will help make it shiny and soft as well as adding volume, as egg is high in vitamins B, D and E. Aloe vera is good for nourishing and repairing. If you do not have aloe vera available you can use avocado, which is rich in vitamin E.

- 1 leaf aloe vera or 1 avocado
- 1 egg

Remove the skin from the aloe vera/avocado. Place the aloe vera/ avocado with the egg in a blender and mix together.

1. Wash your hair first with your regular shampoo. Do not use a 2-in-1 shampoo and conditioner, as this may prevent the absorption to the hair follicles.
2. Rinse your hair with cold water. It is important that you use cold water only, as hot water will start to cook the egg and you will end up with scrambled egg in your hair.
3. Apply the treatment by sectioning off the hair to reveal the scalp. Then work the treatment into your hair by taking small sections and work it through to the ends.
4. When you have completed applying the treatment to your entire head, use a wide-toothed comb to ensure that you have coated most of the hair follicles. Start by combing the ends first.
5. Leave the hair treatment on for 15 minutes and if you wish, massage your scalp using the tips of your fingers in small circular movements.
6. When the treatment has been on for 15 minutes, rinse thoroughly with cold water only.

Revitalising facial treatment again using your own natural ingredients you can prepare a luxurious facial. To obtain the full benefits, follow each of these steps for the various stages of the treatment.

Milk cleanser

- 2 ml fresh cold milk
- 2 drops lavender essential oil for combination skin
- or 2 drops chamomile essential oil for sensitive skin.

Store the milk cleanser in the fridge until you are ready to use it, ensuring a full, refreshening effect.

Cucumber and watermelon toner

- 1 cucumber
- 1/4 watermelon

Juice the watermelon in a blender, taking care to remove the pips. Cut two thin slices of cucumber (for the eyes). Remove the skin from the remaining cucumber, place in the blender and blend with the watermelon.

Strawberry scrub and mask

- 10 strawberries
- 15 ml natural yoghurt

Place the strawberries and the yoghurt in a blender and mix together into a smooth paste. Try to make sure the pips are still present as this will act as an exfoliant.

Vapour bowl

- 1 large bowl
- 1 large towel
- 3 drops lavender oil
- 3 drops eucalyptus oil

A vapour bowl will help to open your pores in preparation for the facial mask. Eucalyptus is good for respiratory problems, cleansing and purifying. Lavender is good for healing, exhaustion and depression.

Aromatherapy face massage oil

- 3 drops eucalyptus oil
- 3 drops lavender oil
- 10 ml almond oil

Mix the oils together and store in an amber-tinted glass bottle to keep the quality of the oils.

Method

1. Apply a small amount of milk cleanser on cotton wool pads and wipe over the face and neck area. This will remove any excess oil without stripping the skin.
2. Place a small amount of the cucumber and watermelon toner onto cotton wool pads and wipe over your face and neck to remove any excess cleanser.
3. Apply a small amount of the strawberry mask in your hand and very gently exfoliate your skin using the tips of your fingers. Do not press too hard, as this will damage the skin. When using any exfoliant minimum pressure should always be applied.
4. Rinse your face with warm water.
5. Wipe over your face and neck with the watermelon and cucumber toner to remove any excess exfoliant.
6. Add boiling hot water to the prepared vapour bowl. Tie your hair back and place a large towel to trap the steam. Do not hold your face too close to the water as it can cause broken capillaries. Make sure that it feels warm but not too hot. Use the vapour bowl for 10 minutes. This will help to open the pores ready for the nourishing mask.
7. Pat your face dry with a clean towel and then apply the strawberry mask over your face and neck. Leave on for 15-20 minutes. This will hydrate and cleanse the skin.
8. Place the two cucumber slices over your eyes to help soothe dark circles and puffiness.
9. Remove the mask with warm water and follow with the watermelon and cucumber toner to remove excess mask.
10. Apply a small amount of aromatherapy face massage oil into your hands and massage the skin, avoiding the eye area. Use light stroking movements working from the centre of the face outwards. This will help to stimulate your circulation, improving the general appearance of your skin.
11. Try to leave the oil on, as this will nourish your skin.

NATURAL BODY CARE

Take time out with luxurious yet simple preparations that are good for the body and the mind.

Honey scrub

Before you start any body treatment it is important that you remove the surface dead skin cells on your body. This will not only make your skin feel smooth, it will also allow any treatment you apply afterwards to absorb much better, making the most of each product.

- 100 ml oatmeal
- 60 ml honey
- 3 drops lavender oil

Mix the ingredients in a blender, ensuring that the oatmeal is not blended in completely.

Oats are high in vitamin E, an antioxidant which helps the formation of red blood cells. As an antioxidant, it helps destroy or neutralise free radicals. This plays a role in slowing the aging process. When applied to the skin it keeps the skin's natural moisture.

Honey helps to cleanse the skin and remove dead skin cells, as it forms a sticky residue on the skin. Lavender relaxes and is healing.

Method

1. Use a dry body brush, starting from the feet and working up your body towards the heart. This will help to remove dead skin cells and stimulate the lymphatic system.

2. Stand in the shower and apply the body scrub on one area at a time. Massage the body scrub into each area until the mixture starts to become tacky. Do this until you have worked all over your body.

3. Take a hot shower to remove the mixture, working the body scrub as you go. It is important that you do not use any soaps or shower gels, as this will dry out your skin.

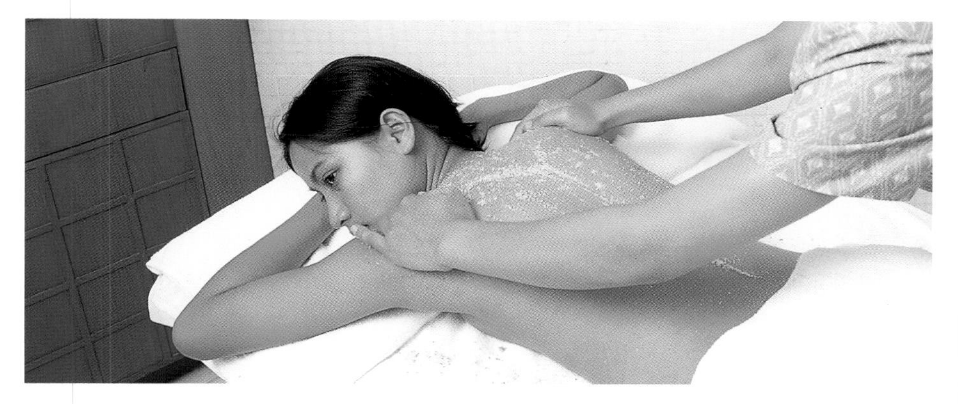

Aromatherapy bath

What better way to wind down than to create your own luxurious bath. All you need are a few simple ingredients.

- 5 of your favourite flowers (we recommend red roses)
- 2 drops geranium oil
- 2 drops lavender oil
- 2 drops ylang ylang oil

Method

1. Run your bath to the desired temperature.
2. While the bath is running, make sure that the lights are dimmed, play your favourite relaxation music and burn a few candles around the tub.
3. When the bath is ready, add the six drops of essential oils. It is important that you do this after the bath has run, as otherwise it may destroy the effectiveness of the essential oils. Consult your doctor first if you have any medical conditions. Pregnant women should not use the recommended essential oils.
4. Sprinkle your flowers whole or just the petals on the surface of the water.
5. Simply lie back and relax. We recommend you stay at least 20 minutes in the bath for the most beneficial effect.

Geranium helps to balance the mind and body, hormonal and emotional swings. It is also an aphrodisiac, promotes sensitivity and relaxation and helps with lethargy and fatigue. Lavender acts as a calming tonic for the nervous system, exhaustion and depression, and also relieves headaches and migraines. Ylang ylang is an aphrodisiac: it uplifts and relaxes, deals with frustration, anxiety and depression, and also helps with insomnia.

Aromatherapy moisturiser

- 1 drop lavender oil
- 1 drop geranium oil
- 1 drop ylang ylang oil
- 40 ml almond oil

Simply mix the oils together to make your own aromatherapy moisturiser.

Massage in all over your body, saving about 10 ml of the moisturiser for the foot and hand treatments.

MANICURE AND PEDICURE

A simple 30-minute manicure and pedicure once a week will help to keep your hands and feet in good condition. Our hands are exposed every day to extreme weather conditions and detergents, and a manicure will help to keep your skin soft and ensure your hands always look well-groomed.

Our feet tend to be one of the most neglected parts of our body. They take a lot of stress every day as they take our whole body weight and are sometimes squeezed into badly-fitting shoes. It is a good idea to let your feet breathe when you are at home to help prevent fungal infections. A treat for your feet on a regular basis will help prevent hard skin, corns and unsightly toenails.

Exfoliant for hands and feet

- 2 tbsp sea salts
- 3 tbsp almond oil

Mix the sea salts and almond oil together and keep in a small bowl.

Hand and foot bath

- 1 pint milk
- 2 drops lavender oil
- Rose petals from 1 red rose

Place the ingredients in one large bowl for the feet and one small bowl for the hands.

Manicure

1. Start by soaking your hands and feet in the prepared hand and foot baths. Relax for at least 10 minutes as this will help to soften the skin, making it easier to work on your cuticles and remove any dry skin from your feet.
2. Work a small amount of the exfoliant into your hands, also massaging around the cuticles.
3. Cut and file your fingernails to the desired length, filing from the outside of the nails into the middle.
4. Massage the aromatherapy moisturiser into the cuticles and push them back with a hoof stick.
5. Finish by massaging a small amount of the aromatherapy moisturiser into the skin on your hands and arms.

Pedicure

1. Remove your feet from the footbath and dry them with a towel.
2. Work the rest of the exfoliant into your feet, massaging around the cuticles and on the soles of the feet.
3. Cut and file your toenails to the desired length, filing from the outside of the nails into the middle. Your toenails should be straight, not curved, in order to prevent ingrown toenails.
4. Massage the aromatherapy moisturiser into the cuticles and push them back with a hoof stick.
5. Use a foot pumice to remove dry skin on the soles of the feet and any excess hard skin. Rinse them in the foot bowl and dry off with a clean towel.
6. Finish by massaging the remaining aromatherapy moisturiser into the skin on your feet and calves.
7. Put on a pair of comfortable socks to allow the moisturiser to penetrate.

Components

We all are made up of three components: body, mind and spirit. Corresponding to these are three needs that must be satisfied for a contented life. The physical need is health, the psychological need is knowledge, and the spiritual need is inner peace. When all are achieved the result is a balance, or harmony, within our bodies.

Most forms of exercise will help the physical need. This revolves around the three main areas of cardiovascular, or heart fitness; strength, for the muscles; and flexibility, the range of motion for joints and muscles. The psychological and spiritual needs of our bodies can also be met through some new exercise techniques.

One important aspect of a successful exercise programme is to leave aside the notion that the weight of your body is the best indicator of fitness. It is far better to measure your progress using body composition analysis, rather than total weight change. What does this mean? Body composition refers to the amount of lean and fat tissue that makes up total body weight. Lean comprises muscle, bone and water.

2 of fitness

CYBEX
TWINS

Whatever the total weight, lean and fat proportions need to be within established, recommended limits in order to avoid the many health problems associated with being over fat. These include high blood pressure, high cholesterol levels, arteriosclerosis, coronary disease and respiratory disorders and dysfunction. Equally serious is the problem of having too little body fat, since adipose tissue is essential for normal organic functions.

The dramatic increase in anorexia nervosa, bulimia and the fear of obesity over the last decade indicates that an increased awareness of correct body composition is of vital importance to us all. If you don't have access to proper body composition measuring devices then a simple measuring tape can be used on relevant areas of the body. As your fitness programme progresses you will notice changes in shape and size that are relative to changes in your composition.

Body fat is therefore more important in weight management programmes than actual weight. Traditional diets can cause people to reduce muscle tissue along with body fat, which slows metabolism. Studies have revealed that a combination of aerobic exercise and strength training with a low-fat diet burns body fat tissue while maintaining lean muscle. In addition, the amount of lean muscle tissue in the subjects actually increased. Quite simply, fatty components and not total weight determine susceptibility to health risks. With this in mind, and having undergone a thorough medical check-up, you can begin your new fitness programme.

CARDIOVASCULAR FITNESS

The benefits of improving cardiovascular fitness are many and varied. They include decreasing the risk of developing cardiovascular disease, weight management and the avoidance of obesity, reduction and management of hypertension and high cholesterol, improved heart function, reduction of stress and anxiety, and management of metabolic disorders such as diabetes.

A successful cardiovascular programme needs to follow some general guidelines to ensure maximum safety and effectiveness. These are the frequency and intensity of your exercise, the type of exercises you perform and the time you actually spend doing the exercise.

As a general guideline, the American College of Sports Medicine recommends an exercise intensity of between 60 and 90 percent of maximum predicted heart rate (220 minus your age). This is based on apparently healthy individuals who have no contra-indications to exercise. Very unfit individuals, however, have achieved benefits from as little as 50 to 60 percent of their maximum heart rate.

There is another way of judging your exercise intensity that is even easier than measuring heart rates. This is called the Talk Test. Quite simply, if you cannot hold a light conversation while you are exercising because you are too breathless, then you are working too hard and your intensity is too high. If anyone has any contra-indications to physical activity, they need to consult a professional before commencing an exercise programme.

What type of exercises should you take? That is the beauty of fitness – there are so many activities you can choose from. The most obvious form of exercise for strength is weight training, but similar gains can also be achieved through activities such as aerobics, yoga, Pilates, fit-balls and therabands. Many day-to-day manual tasks can also be the focus for strengthening programmes. Forms of cardiovascular fitness cover an even wider range, with options both indoors and out, machine-assisted as with treadmills and bicycles, or powered purely by the body, as with running or swimming.

As far as time is concerned for your exercise, 20 to 60 minutes of continuous exercise should be completed in one session. Very unfit individuals can achieve cardiovascular benefits from as little as 10 minutes of exercise. The frequency of your exercise period is recommended as a minimum of three times a week for any improvement to take place.

Cardiovascular fitness best describes the health and function of the heart, lungs and circulatory system. It also describes the capacity of the lungs to exchange oxygen and carbon dioxide with the blood, and to transport nutrients and waste products to and from the body's active tissues.

FLEXIBILITY

The benefits of stretching to improve flexibility and overall condition are becoming more and more evident in the fitness world. Ask any accomplished athlete the secrets of his or her success and you will almost always hear stretching referred to. So if stretching can benefit sports people who subject their bodies to extreme training conditions, why not any body?

Some of the benefits that can be gained are reduced muscle tension, increased relaxation, aid in the prevention of injury, stimulation of blood circulation, development of body awareness and faster recovery after strenuous exercise. Stretching can be done at any time of the day, and anywhere, including while watching television, waiting for the bus and sitting at your desk. It is a good way to relieve physical and emotional tension.

Static stretching is the most commonly practised and safest technique. As the name suggests, it involves a lengthening of the muscle which is held without bouncing for about 20 seconds. The feeling of mild tension felt at this level should subside during the duration of the stretch.

Stretching should be performed before and after exercise. Prior to exercise stretching allows increased blood flow and therefore oxygen to the muscles. It excites the muscles in preparation for the activity to come. On completion of exercise the muscles that have been working need to be reminded what the "relaxed" position is, and stretching achieves this.

A few basic principles to watch are to breathe normally when holding the stretch; don't bounce but rather move slowly into the stretch; hold at the maximum point of comfort; and stretch to your own limits.

Use of weights or a similar form of resistance can produce benefits above and beyond pure aerobic cardiovascular exercise. Not only do the strength gains improve the average person's functional capacity, but it is also a very important part of weight management. The increased muscle tissue from strength training (even small amounts) improves metabolism which in turn enhances the rate your body burns fuel during exercise. Research has found that your metabolism will remain elevated after completion of a resistance workout, meaning you continue to burn calories even when resting!

STRENGTH TRAINING

Resistance training increases bone mineral density, helping to reduce the risk of osteoporosis and bone fractures. Stronger bones mean the body is better equipped to resist degenerative changes usually associated with ageing, such as muscle loss (which slows metabolism), weakened bones and loss of coordination. The overall effect is a stronger, healthier body, with less chance of suffering from conditions such as weight gain, heart disease, hypertension and high cholesterol. These conditions can all actually be managed through resistance training when combined with other lifestyle modifications, if they have already become a problem.

Any exercise increases the flow of blood around your body. Resistance training improves blood circulation by making your muscles work harder. The transportation of nutrients to these muscles is increased and the removal of waste products improved, as the continual movement of the blood supply is at a much greater rate. People recovering from injuries who undergo resistance rehabilitation programmes find that the increased blood circulation is one of the avenues to faster recovery.

Skeletal and muscular imbalances can be corrected by training against a resistance in those areas that are weak. Once irregularities have been ironed out, improvements in coordination and balance will follow naturally. This extends to flexibility and range of motion (ROM). Combining resistance training with stretching aims to promote blood circulation, prevent muscle and joint injuries, and increase the ROM through which the body can bend, flex, extend and reach more easily. Your day-to-day movements become freer and easier, chores become less irksome, and your attitude to all forms of work and activity will hopefully become more positive!

Resistance training leads on to the concept of body sculpting. This is so often thought of as a pursuit of the superbly fit, but essentially body sculpting is a term encompassing all forms of training to get you looking, and consequently feeling, your best.

There is no such thing however as a fast-track programme. It takes a lot of time and focus to achieve your goal, and to maintain it. Further, it is very important to choose something that is realistic and achievable. On the way to your ultimate goal, you need to choose shorter-term goals that can be accomplished without huge amounts of effort. Achieving the smaller goals provides encouragement to continue to the next level, and eventually your final goal. Your first goal might be as simple as losing 2kg, the next may be to walk for 5km without stopping. Take it one stage at a time and be patient.

THERABAND STRENGTHENING EXERCISES

EXERCISE	TECHNIQUE	DIAGRAM	EXERCISE	TECHNIQUE	DIAGRAM
Bicep Curl	Stand on the middle of the theraband with your feet about hip width apart. Grasp the ends of the band in each hand. Keep your upper arm still as you curl the lower arm up. Keep your shoulders and back straight.		**Tricep Kickback**	Position body over a table or bench, one foot forward for stability. Hold on to the table and the band with one hand. Hold other end of the band with free arm. Keep the upper part of this arm parallel with the floor (arm bent). Straighten the arm to create tension on the band.	
Lateral Raise	Position yourself as for bicep curl. Grasp the ends of the band in each hand, with your elbow angle at about 130 degrees slowly raise your arms out to the side until they are horizontal. Keep your shoulders and back straight, keep the movement slow and controlled.	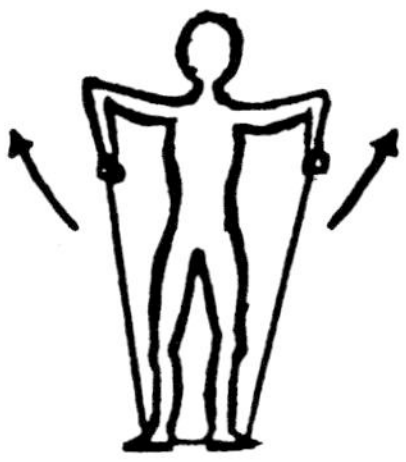	**Theraband Squat**	Stand on the middle of the band with feet shoulder width apart and toes facing forward. Hold one end of the theraband in each hand. Squat down into a sitting position, until your upper leg is parallel with the ground. Raise hands to shoulder height at the same time.	
Lying Tricep Pushdown	Lie on your back with the theraband wrapped around a pole above your head (arms outstretched). Hold one end of the band in each hand, pull the band down until your elbows are on the ground. Push hands down to the floor and repeat.		**Lying Chest Press**	Lie on your back with theraband under the shoulder blades. Hold on to an end of the theraband in each hand. Bend the arms out to the sides so that your elbows are at shoulder level. Carry out the exercise by straightening the arms.	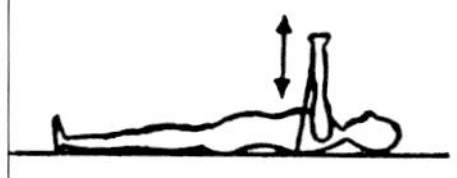
Assisted Sit-ups	Loop the band around something about a metre off the ground. Lie with knees bent and end of the theraband in each hand. Draw your stomach in and perform a sit-up. The further you sit away from the band the more it helps you.	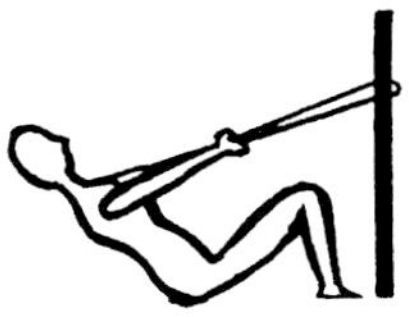	**Hip Abduction / Adduction**	Tie the theraband around your leg and a pole. For the inner thigh, your outer thigh should face the pole. Keep the hips square throughout movement, and bring the tied leg across the body to create tension on the band. To work the outer thigh, have your inner thigh face the pole.	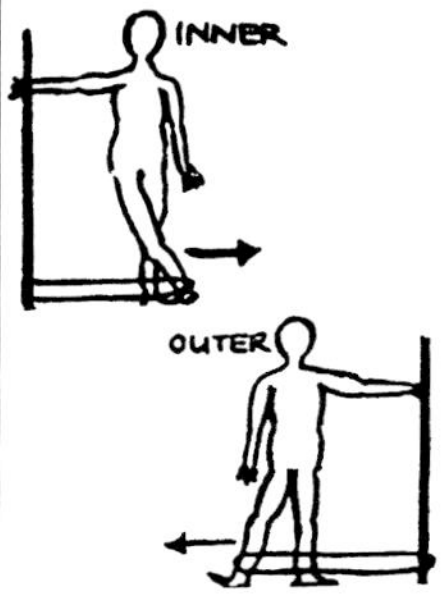
Upright Row	Stand with one foot in the middle of the band, slightly in front of other foot. Hold ends of the band in each hand, thumbs together and palms facing the body. Pull band up to point where elbows and shoulders are level, keeping thumbs together.	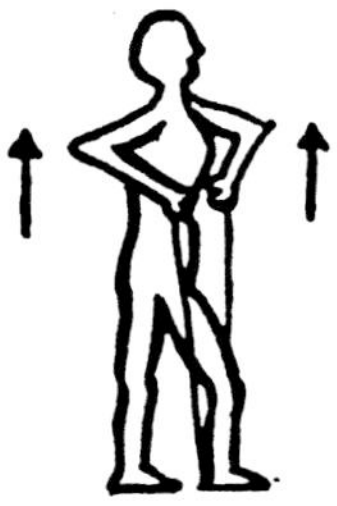	**Chariot Pull**	Loop the band around something fixed about one metre off the ground. Kneel facing the band with one end grasped in each hand, and your abdominal muscles contracted. With straight arms draw the band down to your sides.	
Seated Row	Wrap the band around a table leg or something similar. Sit facing the table leg with knees slightly bent. Grasp the band in both hands, and pull it towards your lower chest. Ensure your shoulders are back and down.		**Shoulder Press**	Stand with both feet on the band and grip either end. Lift hands to shoulder height with palms facing forwards. Press your hands straight up towards the ceiling. Keep your back straight.	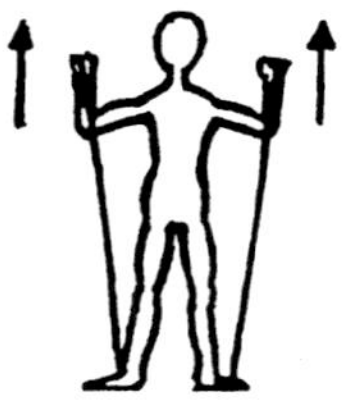

FITNESS OF BODY AND MIND

So closely linked are physical and mental fitness, that techniques to develop both of these areas have become increasingly popular in recent times, and are often intertwined.

The Pilates technique is an outstanding example. Originally developed by German-born Joseph Pilates, it is a unique form of conditioning exercise, catering to the specific needs of each individual. Slow, precise movements enable you to become more sensitive to your body's weaknesses and postural misalignment caused by muscular imbalance. The focus is on control and stability, not power, specifically recruiting the deep muscles of the abdomen and lower back.

Physiotherapists and Osteopaths the world over refer patients, including sufferers of back pain and elite athletes, to safely work out under the supervision of highly-trained Pilates teachers, producing unparalleled results. Increased flexibility, strength and an impressive set of abdominals are just a few of the benefits, and the mental focus combined with controlled breathing allows the process to become a meditative and pleasurable experience. With these elements, and the creation of flowing movements and postural awareness, the Pilates method provides a highly effective mind-body workout.

Another highly enjoyable way of working the mind and body is the use of Fit balls. Fit balls, Swiss balls, physio balls – call them what you will, these big blow-up balls of different sizes and colours are becoming a favoured tool of the personal trainer and a "must-have" piece of equipment for the home studio.

Fit balls are amongst the most effective exercise apparatus for helping relieve lower back pain and developing spinal, pelvic and shoulder girdle stability. Total core stability is achieved, along with improved posture and an increased awareness of your own body – the way it moves and the way it is designed to move. Using Fit balls can also add variety and fun to create new and challenging demands on the body in a number of different planes.

FIT BALLS & CHI BALLS

The right size Fit ball is determined by your height and more importantly your leg length. While sitting on top of the ball, with calves perpendicular to the ground, your thighs should be parallel and at 90-100 degrees, with your knees and your body weight evenly distributed over both feet. This is your correct postural position. Imagine a straight line starting from your ear, travelling through your shoulder and stopping at the centre point of your pelvis. This visual connection will help you adjust and maintain correct postural alignment in the initial stages of learning with the Fit ball. As with all exercises, the quality of movement is more important than the quantity of exercise.

Chi ball is a form of exercise that embraces the philosophies of both the East and the West to improve overall health, happiness and wellbeing. Devised by Monica Linford in the early 1990s, the method is perhaps best described as aromatherapy and balance in motion. Chi balls help tone and balance the body, mind and spirit through simple, yet effective, exercises.

A Chi ball class is designed to teach the participants to feel and understand the concept of balance through yin and yang. Each element is used to create awareness of the body's holding patterns and level of energy (chi). There are five elements: Traditional Chinese Medicine to rebalance and harmonise the meridian system (rising and radiant yang). Yoga postures to build strength, stability, flexibility and consolidate the chi (radiant and descending yang). Pilates to improve awareness of posture, teach central strength and stability of the spine and begin settling the chi through breathing (descending yang and rising yin). The Feldenkrais Technique, to release tension from the body and promote flexibility and awareness and thus calm and soften the chi (rising yin). And finally Deep Relaxation to bring the chi to its lowest level (condensed yin) for harmony, good health and well being – the natural state of being.

The different coloured Chi balls are all impregnated with a different aromatherapy scent. Yellow balls have lemongrass oil to tone the nervous system, stabilise the emotions, release anxiety and uplift the spirit. Orange balls contain orange oil for joy, exuberance and confidence. Green balls have geranium oil to ease frustration and irritability and promote harmony and relaxation of the mind and emotions. Purple balls contain lavender oil to promote self-expression and soothe, calm and relax the body, mind and spirit.

FIT BALL TRAINING: BASIC EXERCISE PROGRAMME

EXERCISE	TECHNIQUE	DIAGRAM	ALTERNATIVES	EXERCISE	TECHNIQUE	DIAGRAM	ALTERNATIVES
Lower Abdominals	Place the ball in between your legs. Don't squeeze too hard. Place your fingers under your back, directly below the belly button. Maintain a neutral spine, apply pressure against your fingers while bringing the ball towards your chest. Hold and release.		Use a medicine ball. Vary the tempo (speed). Don't use a ball.	**Bridge**	Get into a squatting position with the ball between your shoulder blades. Push up through your heels until your head rests on the ball and squeeze your gluteals. Keep the abdominals strong and body horizontal. Hold this for several seconds, and repeat.		Place a ball between your knees to enhance recruitment of adductors. Go up onto your toes to recruit calves.
Oblique Abdominals	Lie on the ball with your knees at 90 degrees and thigh parallel with the floor. Allow your spine to move into complete flexion. With your hands on your thighs, contract the abs and reach for each calf, one at a time. Hold the position and return to a fully relaxed state.		Upper abdominal exercise while supporting the head.	**Supine Knee Raise**	Lie on your back, with the ball between your shoulder blades. Keeping your body straight and your knees at 90 degrees slowly raise one foot several centimetres off the ground and hold for a minimum of three seconds, change legs and repeat.		Moving the ball up your back increases the level of difficulty. Extend the leg. Extend leg and rotate foot.
Upper Abdominals	Lie on the ball with your knees at 90 degrees. Move through the spine's complete range of motion. Contract your abs and bring your rib cage towards your pelvis. Begin with your hands behind your ears and progress to having your arms extended above your head.		Use different hand and arm positions.	**Calf Raise**	Hold the ball against a wall by placing it between your shoulder blades. Keep toes facing forwards and feet shoulder width apart. Move up onto the balls of the feet as high as possible, while using the Fit ball to help support the body. Be sure not to roll ankles in or outwards.		Feet together. Feet apart. Single foot. Rotate the foot clockwise and anti-clockwise.
Back Rest	This exercise can take the weight off your lower back. Lie on the ground with your calves supported by the ball. Make sure your hips and your knees are at 90 degrees. This position can be held from 5 to 25 minutes depending on the amount of relaxation required.		A chair or object of similar height can also be used for this exercise.	**Ball Walkouts**	Kneel down in front of the ball. Roll onto the ball and walk out with your hands so the ball moves towards your shins. Stabilise your trunk and keep your body straight. Do this by holding your tummy in so your spine is lengthened to support your lower back. Hold this position and return to the start.	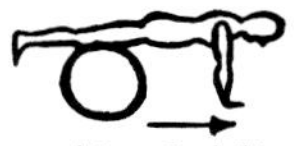	Roll the ball to your feet. Cross your legs before rolling out. Single leg. Push ups. Stabilise with one hand.
Prone Diagonals	Balance yourself over the ball with hands and feet on the ground. Lift one arm up parallel to the floor, hold for 2 seconds. Try each limb in turn. When comfortable with these, lift left arm and right leg up together and return to the floor. Alternate and repeat.		Lie flat on the floor. On your knees. Vary the tempo (speed). Hold the contraction for a longer period of time.	**Push-ups**	Roll yourself over the ball and place your thighs on top of the ball. Stabilise yourself with your arms at 90 degrees to the ground. Complete a push-up by bending at the elbow as far as you can and push back to the starting position. Keep elbows pointing out and aim to place your chin between your index fingers.		Move further away from the ball to increase level of difficulty. Use a medicine ball.
Wall Squats	Place the ball into your lower back and lean against a wall. Lower yourself into a squat position and allow your bottom to follow the curve of the ball. Continue till your thighs are parallel with the ground then push up through your heels. Don't lock out the knees		Hold dumbbells. Move up onto toes to recruit more calves. Reverse and forward lunges holding the fit ball.	**Pelvic Lift**	Lie on your back with heels on the ball. Arms at 90 degrees to the body. Raise your pelvis into the air so only your shoulders are on the ground. Hold this position for several seconds then relax. Ensure your legs are fully extended and the quadriceps are fully contracted.	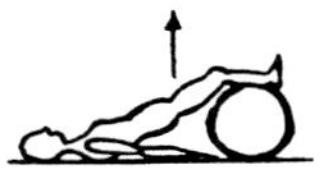	Bring your arms closer to your sides or place them on your chest. Move the ball further away towards your toes.
Free Squat and Press	Hold the ball out in front of you with your feet just outside shoulder width, toes slightly out. Squat down, pushing your bottom out and your body weight through your heels. Holding the ball in front of you will change your centre of gravity and improve balance. Drive up, and push the ball above your head.		Use a medicine ball. Progress to squat rack or Smith machine squat. Stepping lunges. Hamstring flicks. Throw the ball and catch.	**Supine Leg Curls**	Lie on your back, lift body up with heels on the ball. Arms at 90 degrees to the body. Raise your pelvis towards the ceiling so only your shoulders are on the ground. From this position drag your heels in towards your buttocks, hold, and push out again. Allow the bottom to touch the floor and repeat.		Hands on chest. Arms in the air. Single foot. Keep pelvis off floor throughout whole set. Keep pelvis on floor curling legs in without lift.
Sitting Knee Raise	Sit on the ball. Keeping your knees at 90 degrees slowly raise one foot several centimetres off the floor. Ensure you keep your shoulders parallel with the ground, and your abdominals contracted to stabilise the upper body. Alternate between left and right legs, and follow the suggestions at right.		Lift knees and extend leg. Hold the ball (easier). Place your hands on your hips or thighs. Place your hands out in front or in the air.	**Back Extensions**	Stabilise yourself on top of the ball so only your feet are on the ground. Begin with your arms by your sides, thumbs pointing inwards. As you exhale, extend towards the ceiling and externally rotate your arms and squeeze the shoulder blades together.	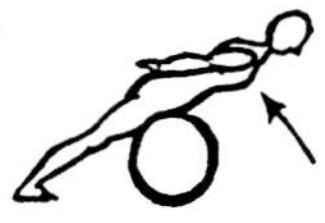	Hands under chin or extended above head. Arms by sides, externally rotate arms to squeeze shoulder blades together. Change the tempo (speed).
Wall Push-up	Hold the Fit ball against the wall at chest height with both hands shoulder width apart. Move feet back so you are slightly leaning into the ball. Begin the movement by bending at the elbows and bringing your chest in to within 2-3 inches of the ball, and complete by pushing against the ball to bring yourself back to the initial position.	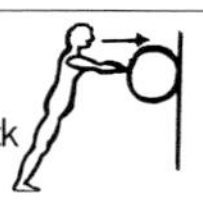	Do the exercise against a large pole instead of a wall for increased difficulty with stability.	**Sea Urchin**	Follow the same procedure for walkouts but only proceed until your knees are on top of the ball. Ensure your shoulder blades are down and together. Stabilise your upper body and bring your knees towards your chest, tucking into a tight ball, focusing on your lower abdominals. Hold the contraction and return to start.		Move further from the ball. Change the speed of the movement. Slower is harder.

Perform ALL your strength training on the ball – use it as your bench for spine exercises and chair for upright exercises. It is excellent for core stability, balance, mobility and improving posture. Use it as your office chair – this will help to feed your spine, keep it hydrated and enhance circulation of blood and oxygen through the tissues, reducing muscle tension and discomfort.

Maintain smooth, controlled movements with no momentum – this ensures complete fatigue and adaptation. Don't lock your fingers behind your neck when doing abdominal exercises – strengthen your neck as well as your abdominals. Combine wall squats with lateral (side) raises, or bicep curls. Even try bench dips with your feet on the ball.

Tai chi, practised throughout large parts of Asia and increasingly in the West, has its roots in ancient China. It is very suitable for those suffering from everyday tension, having the advantage of being a regular form of exercise combined with a definite emphasis on the gracefulness and slowness of pace that stressful society so conspicuously lacks. Tai chi can give those who live in industrialised, fast-paced cities a compensating factor in their lives. It relaxes the mind as well as the body. It helps digestion, quietens the nervous system, benefits the heart and blood circulation, loosens joints and refreshes the skin.

TAI CHI

Any age group can practise tai chi. Initially one needs a large space, but more advanced students need only four square feet of exercise area. The movements can be performed without any equipment. Appropriate in any season of the year and in any weather, tai chi is unlimited in its benefits and the conditions in which it reveals its nature. It is best to practise the forms twice a day: in the morning when arising and in the evening before retiring. Many also find it soothing and refreshing to do in the office during lunchtime.

Throughout the world tai chi is performed for a variety of reasons. Dance and theatre schools use it as part of their training routines. Medical institutions in China use it as an aid to restoring health. In New York it is taught in homes for the aged. For daily exercise and maintaining health it is an ideal regimen.

Tai chi can help both men and women enhance their personal appearance. Beauty is not confined to the face, but permeates the whole body. The relaxed, gentle movements of tai chi keep the body from being tense and awkward. The forms also keep the body erect and well postured. Muscular tension drains an adequate supply of blood from the fine blood vessels of the face and hands, and the relief provided by tai chi corrects this condition, pouring colour and life into neglected parts. Adequate oxygen and blood circulation prevents a person from appearing old.

There are many schools of tai chi. The Yang School has great influence in Chinese society and is also the most popular, both in China and abroad. The high forms, in which the body is kept upright, are best for the beginner and the older person. The more advanced student should use the low forms, with large steps and low-postured body, necessitating particularly loose joints and flexible limbs. The middle forms are suitable for the average student.

The long routine of the Yang School has 108 different postures, and lasts from 15 to 20 minutes when fully comprehended. This is for the advanced tai chi student. The short routine, recommended for the average student, is much easier to learn as it comprises only about 50 forms and takes from seven to 10 minutes or less to perform a full sequence. It is good for the office worker and for people who wish to improve their health, and can be practised two or three times a day.

If you wish to learn tai chi, first you must be positively determined in mind. In order to achieve proficiency, daily practice is desirable. It must become an essential part of your life. Second, you should find a good teacher to give you a combination of correct forms and the deep philosophy underlying it, inspiring you to achieve the strong yet subtle concentration necessary.

WATSU

Watsu is another new exercise technique combining modern methods with ancient. It is actually a form of massage named from the combination of WATer and ShiatSU, and was devised when Harold Dull started floating people at the Harbin Hot Springs in California, applying the moves and stretches of Zen shiatsu.

While being cradled by the practitioner, and with the buoyancy of the warm water, you are moved through a dance-like sequence of stretches combined with moments of stillness. These are coordinated with the way the body moves naturally in the water, and with the rhythm of the breath. The freeing of the spine is the basis of a Watsu session, as the body is moved in ways that are not possible on land.

The stretches and rotations of the arms and legs open up the meridians that flow through them, so the energy pathway of the spine is encouraged to clear. As the water takes the weight off the vertebrae and joints, and relaxes the muscles, new life is infused into long-neglected connective tissue. This removes excess pressure on the nerves and improves the tone and functioning of the whole body and the organs those nerves serve. Unrestricted by contraction, the circulation can carry away metabolites left over in the muscles, thereby reducing soreness and fatigue. The reduced requirements of oxygen in states of weightlessness help to calm the respiratory and nervous systems.

Watsu is not only liberating physically. The mind, freed from physical stress, can quieten itself into what many describe as a feeling of nurturing: peace and lightness of spirit. It is not uncommon for emotions to be released during a session.

Research shows that under stress the heart's electromagnetic waves become erratic and uncoordinated. In this chaotic state the immune system is weakened by our sympathetic "fight or flight" nervous system becoming over-activated. Just as the water accepts everything in its path, the practitioner accepts and adapts to the subject, thereby inducing the kinds of feelings often felt during Watsu – care, appreciation, acceptance. Under these circumstances the heart's rhythms come into what scientists describe as coherence, allowing emotions to be integrated, the nervous system to attain balance and the immune system to strengthen.

Watsu is used around the world to treat a number of diseases and disorders including stress and anxiety-related conditions, chronic back pain, orthopaedic problems, arthritis, insomnia, depression, headaches and hyperactivity.

You may wonder if walking is a really effective form of exercise. Fit people may think walking is too easy, overweight people may wonder if they really can become trim by walking, and people recovering from surgery or medical conditions wonder if walking is safe.

WALKING FOR FITNESS

The answer to these questions is that brisk walking is an aerobic activity, so walking at the right pace can give you all the benefits of other sports. It helps you burn fat, and is one of the safest forms of exercise if you are under medical care.

We take walking for granted. We do it every day, taking dozens if not hundreds of trips to the kitchen, car, bathroom, around the office, to the stores and so on. So a programme of walking needs no great adjustment to our general lifestyle. If you lead an inactive life and are a bit out of shape, walking exercise could be just what you need. Not too taxing, yet providing the fitness benefits.

Walking burns calories and improves muscle tone, helping to firm and shape muscles in your hips, legs, buttocks and abdomen. It is a valuable part of a weight-loss programme. Walking increases bone density, and according to recent research may lower the risk of osteoporosis. And of course it can also be a tonic for the mind as well as the body, helping to relieve stress and allowing you to unwind at the end of the day.

Before beginning your walking programme, decide what your goals are. If you have been inactive for a long period of time or have chronic health problems, you should consult your physician before commencing. Plan on a minimum of three walks a week on alternating days and of 20 minutes or more each time.

To get the most benefit from your walking you need to work at an intensity of about 70 percent of your target heart rate. It is not a complicated formula – just subtract your age from 220 and multiply the answer by 70 percent. Taking your pulse at regular intervals during your walk, or wearing a heart-rate monitor, will allow you to keep within your target range.

Ideally, a safe and effective walk workout consists of a warm-up with stretching, and a post-exercise cool down with more stretching. Before, during and after exercise you need to drink plenty of water in order to maintain your normal body temperature and cool down the working muscles. If you are planning on walking regularly, invest in a pair of comfortable, supportive walking shoes.

TRAVEL TRAINING

In response to the question "What sort of regular exercise do you do?" many people reply, "None – I don't have the time". It is true that so many of us have very heavy work or travel commitments, but a personal programme can be devised that will enable anyone to tone up, even when rushing from one part of the globe to another. The feeling of wellbeing that can be achieved will only add to the effectiveness and productivity of your working lifestyle.

All that is required is for you to add a Fit ball and/or Therabands to your list of essential luggage items. There is no need for you to find a fitness centre when you are travelling. The corner of your hotel room is enough to set up the Fit ball, which will deflate to such a small size you can pop it comfortably into even an overnight bag.

It's not just the businessperson who experiences the stresses and strains of frequent and rapid air travel. Tourists, endeavouring to get away from the stress of home and work, often subject themselves to many weary hours of airport lounges, cramped seats and airline food. And whether business or pleasure, long-haul travel affects a majority of travellers, to some degree, in the form of jet lag. Is it more than just feeling tired? Yes. Other symptoms include exhaustion, depression and mood swings, confusion, sleeplessness at night, headaches, loss of appetite at meal times, constipation, peptic ulcers, dehydration and dry skin.

To help avoid jet lag and the other discomforts of a long flight, try these travel tips.

- Get plenty of exercise before your flight. If possible, schedule your travel for afternoon, evening or night so that you will have time for a morning walk or workout routine on that day.

- Order ahead for meals. Nearly all airlines can provide alternative meals, such as a fruit plate, and vegetarian dishes.

- Eat only light foods such as salads and fruit the day before a flight and just eat fruit or a light meal during the flight itself.

- Drink plenty of water (non-carbonated) on the day of travel, prior to getting on the plane.

- Drink plenty of water (non-carbonated) during the flight to restore body fluids which are lost very quickly in the dry cabin air.

- Avoid alcohol – its effects are twice as potent in the aeroplane cabin. It also interferes with your body's ability to use oxygen.

- Always sit in the non-smoking section. Cigarette smoke is particularly irritating to the mucous membranes in the throat, sinuses and eyes, besides being terrible for your lungs.

- Get up and stretch your legs and back at regular intervals.

- Do simple exercises such as ankle rotations (six times in each direction) then point and flex your feet six times. Repeat this many times during the flight.

- Cleanse and tone your skin at the beginning of the flight and use a good moisturising cream. Use as little make-up as possible. Try an Evian-type water spritzer and use frequently on the face during the flight.

- Bring your own small pillow to provide better support for your head while sleeping.

- Use earplugs and eye covers if these will help you sleep during night flights.

- Bring a good book, which will allow you to catch up on your reading. Regard it as a great plus to be able to sit and read without interruption.

Once you reach your destination, you can follow these simple exercises with your Fit ball and Theraband to keep yourself in fine shape without having to look for a fitness centre. You will find yourself feeling fresh and glowing with good health, no matter how far away from home you are!

TRAVEL TRAINING EXERCISES

LEGS: GLUTEALS - Lunge

With legs shoulder-width apart, head up, and back straight, step forward, bending the leg until thigh is parallel to floor.
Return and alternate legs.

Complete 15-25 times.
Do 2 sets.

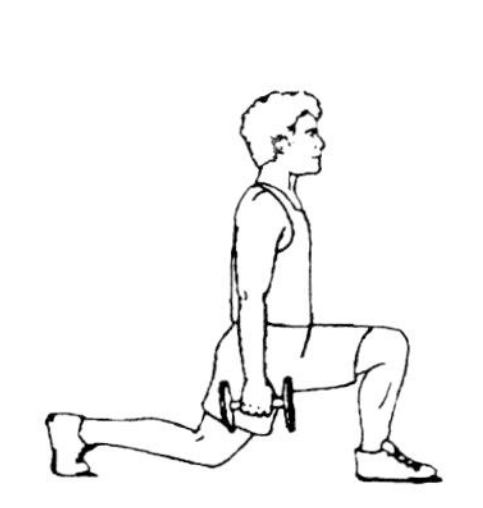

LEGS: ADDUCTORS - Weighted Single-Leg Adduction

From starting position, lift leg as high as possible. Complete all repetitions with one leg first, then repeat with other leg.

Complete 15-20 repetitions.
Do 2 sets.

LEGS: ABDUCTORS - Weighted Single-Leg Abduction

From starting position, sweep leg upward as far as possible. Complete all repetitions with one leg first, then repeat with other leg.

Complete 15-20 repetitions. Do 2 sets.

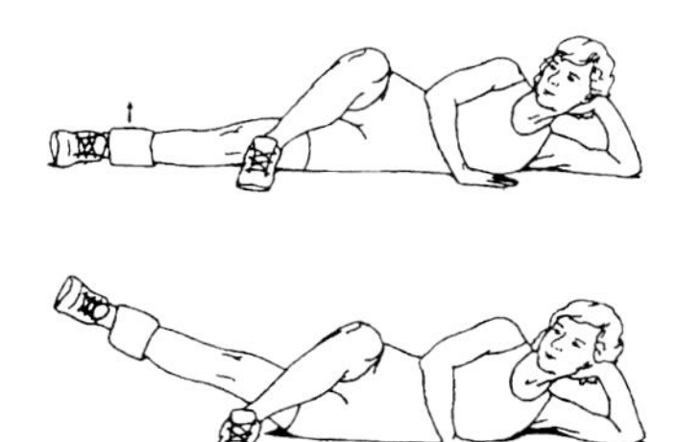

LEGS: GLUTEALS - Squat

Standing on a board with back straight and head looking upward, bend knees until thighs are parallel to floor.

Complete 15-20 repetitions. Do 2 sets.

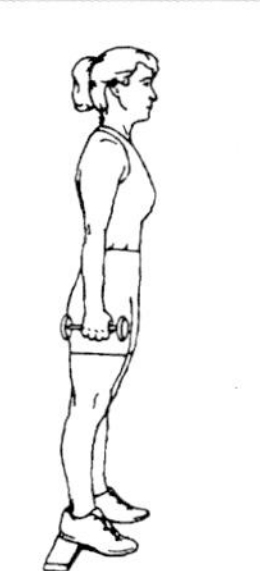

CHEST - Standard Push-up

From starting position, with hands outside shoulder width and with body straight, lower body until chest touches floor.

Do 2 sets.

CHEST - Modified Push-up

From starting position with knees bent, hands outside shoulder width and body straight, lower body until chest touches floor.

Do 2 sets.

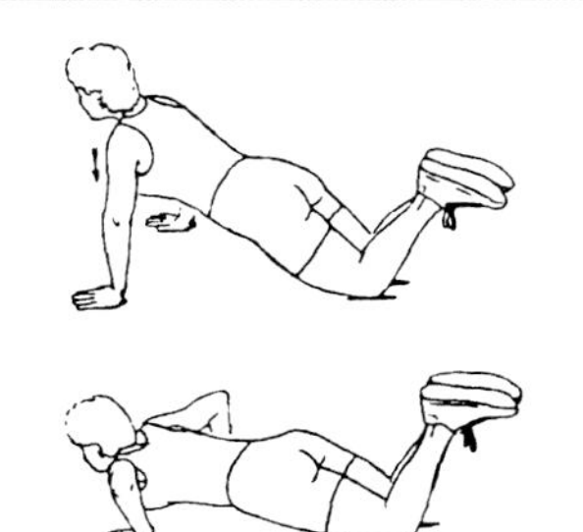

ARMS: TRICEPS - Bench Dip

Keeping elbows close to sides, lower body almost to floor.

Do 2 sets.

ABS - Crunch

Keeping head and neck in line with spine, elevate shoulders and upper back toward knees, keeping low and middle back in touch with floor.

Do 2 sets.

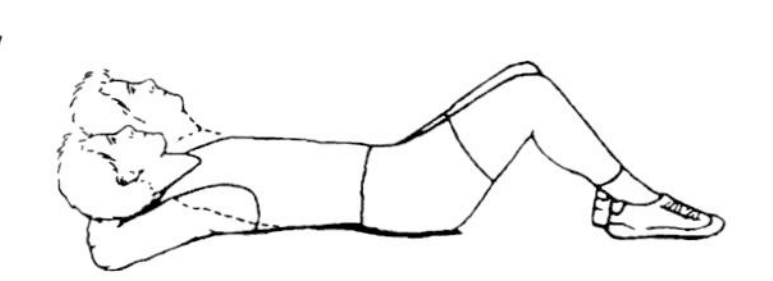

ABS - Alternating Elbow to Knee Touch

Alternate touching right elbow to left knee, and left elbow to right knee.

Do 2 sets.

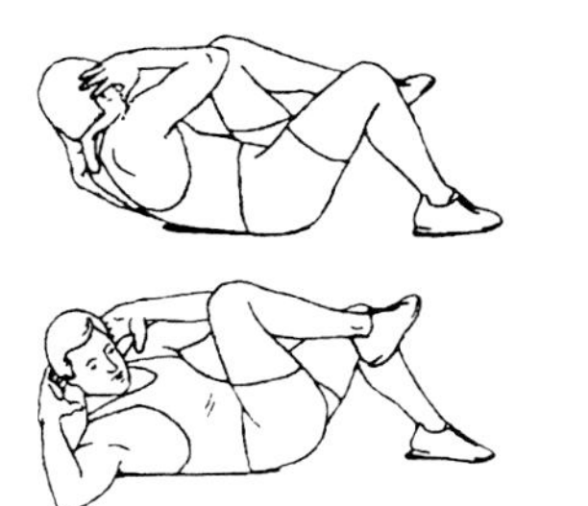

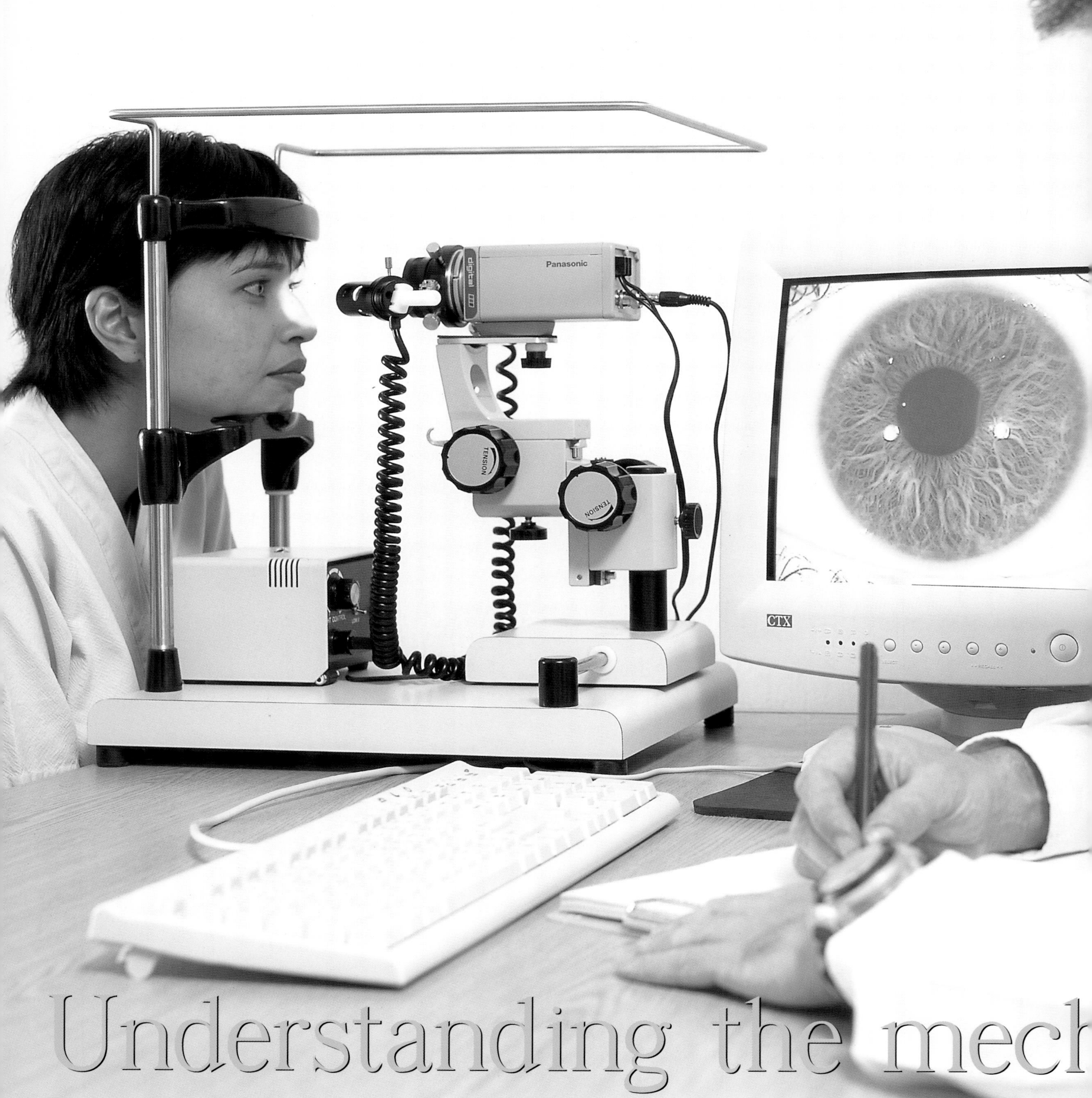

Understanding the mech

We are all ultimately masters of our own minds and bodies, and therefore of our destinies. Understanding how the mechanisms of the body operate is a vitally important step in our positive approach towards physical and mental wellness. The nature of Chiva-Som's own medical programmes is holistic rather than invasive. They have been developed in Europe and elsewhere in the West, but many of them have at their root the traditional medicines and therapies of the East. The main objective of this philosophy is the prevention of illness, or the cure of ailments, by letting the body maintain and heal itself.

Our everyday lives present us with the kind of problems that earlier generations did not have. Our quest is one for a better quality of health and a better quality of life, with more energy and greater vitality; yet we also need an increased ability to cope with the myriad pollutants in our environment, and with often intense stress at home and work. For example, many of our programmes at the resort are designed to combat stress-related illnesses, or are part of a cardiac rehabilitation process. We can also help people in stopping smoking, these days considered a prerequisite for a healthy body.

If you intend, as we hope, to begin now on a new route to health and harmony, we strongly advise that you first undergo a thorough medical examination. Visit your doctor or a health resort, explain your objectives, and ask for a complete physical check-up. This will include not just testing of blood, heart and other organs, but cholesterol, glucose, uric acid and other levels. You will be asked about your lifestyle in general. This will be in effect an analysis of health risk factors, and disease control and prevention. Once you have all this information you can identify your weak points, and start to build your personal programme.

3

...nics of body and mind

CLEANSING DIET AND FASTING: A GOOD START

If you go on a cleansing diet we recommend you choose a simple one that contains only easy to digest foods such as fruit juices, vegetables and herbal teas, which aid in detoxifying the body while still providing the necessary nutrients. You will find that the diet provides you with extra energy, improves the condition of your skin, brightens your eyes and gives extra shine to your hair. It is also naturally a great start to a weight-loss programme.

For a really fresh start, however, a fast is highly recommended. This might sound a drastically alarming step, but it does not need to be nearly as severe or uncomfortable as it might sound.

A good start when you begin your new programme, a cleansing diet or a fast is not only a way of clearing your body of toxins, it is also an important psychological step. Your mind and body will now be telling you that a fresh start has begun, and you will be less inclined to slip back into the old ways. In fact, within a very short space of time you will wonder how you put up with your old way of living for so long.

Toxins build up in the body as a result of the pollutants in the air we breathe, the chemicals in the food and drinks we consume, and many other hazards of modern-day life. Periodically the body seeks to rid itself of these toxins, as they enter the bloodstream. If they stay in the blood for too long, they can cause the body to experience a "low" or "down" cycle.

Fasting is one of the most effective and safest methods of detoxifying and enhancing the healing of the body. During the fast, your body breaks down and removes tissues and cells that are damaged, diseased or inferior, and the elimination of toxins and metabolic wastes that interfere with the nourishment of the cells is increased.

As your fast progresses you will experience symptoms such as bad breath, a coated tongue, dark urine, body odour, nausea, mucous discharge, headaches and skin eruptions. Rest assured that this is all to the good! It is a sure sign that the cleansing process is progressing well. Most of these symptoms can be reduced with the use of vitamin C, which your body will welcome.

Short fasts of one to two days are recommended regularly, whereas longer fasts of five to 10 days can be undertaken once or twice a year. However, when you fast for more than three days, do so only under the supervision of a healthcare professional. Many people like to fast during the spring, finding the psychological aspect particularly pleasing.

Preparation for your fast is important, for you don't simply stop eating and expect nature to take over. It is vital that the pathways for elimination are open, and so the intake of a fibre such as psyllium seed husks, together with extra water, should be consumed at least a week before commencing. A gentle herbal laxative can be taken three days before the fast, and for the first one or two days during the fast. An Epsom salt bath taken daily opens the skin for elimination. Another recommendation is that you eat only raw or lightly cooked fruits and vegetables for three days before beginning.

During your fast, fruit and vegetable juices, herbal teas and vegetable broth should be taken every two to three hours. Juices should be made as fresh as possible, and you can dilute them with 50 percent water. Vegetable broth with natural seasonings such as kelp may be used and all water should be pure filtered water. Tea, coffee, chewing gum, alcohol and cigarettes should be avoided, as should all chemicals, deodorants, sprays, detergents, and synthetic soaps and shampoos.

If you must have something to eat during the fast, eat a piece of watermelon. You can also try fresh raw apple sauce, made in the blender. Strenuous exercise should not be undertaken while you are fasting, and it is best to focus on light exercise such as walking and stretching. Deep breathing exercises and yoga are recommended. When coming off your fast it is suggested that you eat only raw fruits and vegetables for one to two days before resuming your normal diet. If possible, you should also wait for seven to 10 days before consuming animal proteins.

NATUROPATHIC CONSULTATION AND HOLISTIC TREATMENTS

As we begin to realise that reliance solely on modern medicine is not enough, and that our body should be regarded as a natural part of its environment and indeed as its own self-contained environment, many are turning to naturopathic consultation. This can be a more natural, less invasive and often less traumatic treatment for many conditions. Further, there is no problem in using it in conjunction with your current medical treatments.

The human body is a complex organism with the ability to heal itself if we learn to listen to it and respond by giving it what it really needs. In spite of all the abuse our body endures, whether through exposure to environmental toxins, poor nutrition, smoking, alcohol excess, inactivity or suppressing our emotions, it still usually serves us well for many years before starting to break down. Even then, it will respond to a little help, and continue to function satisfactorily.

The natural therapeutic approach maintains the constant effort of the body's vital life force in the direction of self-cleansing, self-repairing and positive health. The aim of naturopathy is to support this process by treating people, not the disease or merely the symptoms, but by removing the cause and empowering individuals to take an active part in the maintenance of their health. There are an increasing number of naturopathic consultants, and finding one within reach of your home should not present any great difficulty.

"Holistic" is a word that has recently been popularised, but it is not often fully understood and many confuse the meaning with that of alternative medicine. By "alternative medicine" we mean a way of healing without the use of medication, or treatments that differ radically in some other way to mainstream medicine. Consequently, it might sound a little extreme. But this is not correct. Holistic health is actually an approach to life. Rather than focusing on illness or specific parts of the body, holistic considers the whole person and how he or she interacts with his or her environment. It brings all aspects together, so that everything is functioning in the very best way possible.

With holistic health, people accept responsibility for themselves: they take control of their own wellbeing. Therein lies much of the satisfaction. It is not as difficult as it may sound. No matter what their current status of health, anyone can improve their level of wellbeing. After all, every day we make a decision on what we consume, both physically and mentally.

The correct choice of physical consumption is necessary because the cells in our body are constantly being replaced. New cells are built from what is available. Harmful substances or lack of needed building blocks in the body can result in imperfect cells, unable to do what is required to keep that person healthy. Similarly, on the non-physical level, a person's mental attitudes are built up from what they see and hear.

How is holistic health actually practised? There are many ways and means, and it is always important to keep your objective in mind. People are motivated by how good it feels to have lots of energy and enthusiasm for life, knowing that what they are doing that day will allow them to continue to feel this good. When disease and chronic conditions do occur, the holistic health principles can also be applied.

You can regard holistic as being simply your own personal philosophy, or you can take it further by reading books and speaking to specialists. You may also find that your local community facilities will be able to link you up with those who know more.

BIO-ENERGY

Alongside holistic we come across another phrase: "bio-energy." In easily explainable terms, what is it? To understand bio-energy, begin with the thought that everything we are and see are forms of energy.

Here is a quick way to feel your own energy and gain a better insight as to what matter is made of. Hold your left palm in a vertical position, thumb facing towards you. Place your right hand horizontally, with the fingers pointed at the left palm, but with the tips at least six inches away so you don't feel any heat. Now slowly wave the fingers of the right hand up and down as if shooting bullets at the left palm. Immediately you should feel a sensation going up and down the left palm. This is your own energy, and now you have felt it you can better appreciate how bio-energy works.

Around the body exists an energy field known as your aura. This again may sound a little fanciful, but put another way it is an electromagnetic field and is well known to scientists. There are forms of photography that reveal this energy field. Further, it can be manipulated.

In a bio-energy session the therapist will feel the energy field around your body and rebalance it where necessary, in much the same way a massage therapist will feel tension in the muscles and release it. The aura stores information about your life, and the aim of the therapist is to remove any blocks that are in the energy field and rebalance them. These are not solely physical problems but emotional ones as well.

An average energy session lasts for 60 minutes and an initial treatment phase of four sessions is recommended. Once the initial four sessions are completed it is possible to have an entire overview of someone's physical and mental health. In turn, bio-energy balancing supports many forms of treatment including massage, reflexology, chi nei tsang, and equilibropathy. It is a holistic treatment in the truest sense as it works on the body, mind and spirit.

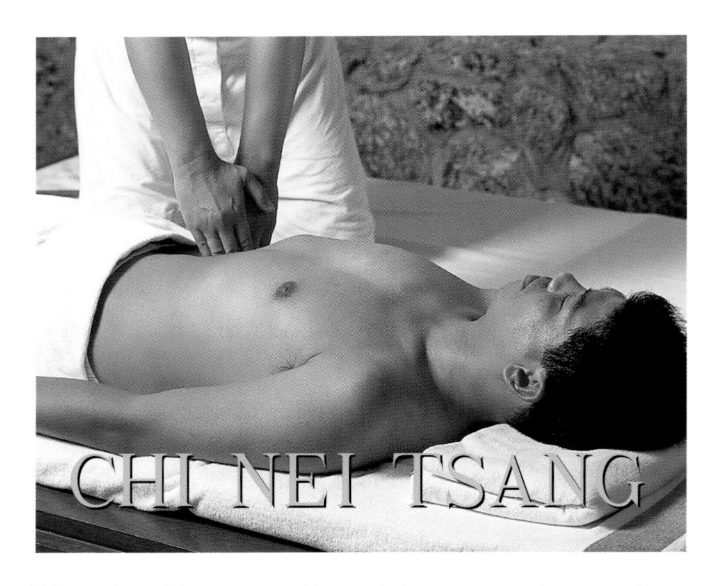

CHI NEI TSANG

Although a bio-energy therapist may resort to modern technology to read your body's aura, chi nei tsang is a traditional Eastern healing art that has evolved alongside Taoist philosophy. Taoists believe that people develop energy blockages in their abdominal area, the centre point for the internal organs. The knots and tangles interrupt the body's vital functions, and the flow of chi, the life force energy, is constricted. Negative emotions such as fear, anger, anxiety, depression and worry cause damage to the body. Overwork, stress, accidents, surgery, drugs, toxins, poor nutrition and bad posture can also cause problems.

When obstructed the internal organs store unhealthy energies that can overflow into other bodily systems and surface as negative emotions and sickness. Always in search of an outlet, they create a perpetual cycle of negativity and stress. If the negative emotions can't find an outlet, they fester in the organs or move into the abdomen, the body's "garbage dump". The abdomen can process some emotional garbage, but more often it can't keep up with the flow. The result is a gradual obstruction of energy circulation that can cause serious damage to your health, impairing physical, mental and spiritual functions.

We can experience this on an everyday level. Each human emotion is an expression of energy and certain emotions can indicate the negative energy behind many physical ailments. You know that sensation of having a "knot" in your stomach? Yes, we all do. It indicates the presence of worry related to a negative emotion, and is an accumulation in the stomach and spleen.

The chi nei tsang practitioner concentrates on massage around the abdominal area, starting from the navel centre, while at the same time guiding the breathing. Once the centre at the navel is activated and freed the body can clear itself of toxins, bad emotions and excessive heat that causes the organs to dysfunction. It is a touch that heals and renews life and spirits.

DIAGNOSTIC TREATMENTS

Recent years have seen the development of an investigational process known as EQ4 meridien testing, which is actually a combination of modern computing science, traditional Chinese medicine, kinesiology, modern chemistry and medical research.

The EQ4 equipment accesses the flow of energy within the body via the meridian channels in the fingers and toes. These points are considered as doorways to the energy of the body, and have been used by acupuncturists to alter the chi flow. The EQ4 does not puncture the skin to obtain information: rather, by introducing an imperceptible electric current it measures the resistance of the acupuncture points.

Commonly about 50 points are tested and an overall snapshot of the organ systems will be obtained. Once the areas of importance are defined the operator can access the vast database of healing remedies to find a treatment that will bring the unbalanced points and meridians back into a state of balance.

This leads us on to another way in which modern technology is enhancing the beliefs and treatments of an earlier era. Iridology is a science whereby the iridologist is able to analyse the condition of various organs and body systems by examining markings and irregularities in fibre structure and colour changes in the iris, providing clues about the state of a person's health. Fundamental to iridology is the old theory that the eyes offer a reliable representation of a person's wellbeing.

In everyday language we often comment on a person's bright or dull eyes. In fact, all our nerve endings are linked to the backs of our irises. Therefore if there is change in a part of the body, a reflex signal is sent along the nerve impulses and is displayed as a change in the iris fibre structure according to that particular body part. Iridology employs a digital/video iriscope, a tool that enables analysis of the eyes while you sit in comfort and view your irises on the computer screen.

GOOD BREATHING

Keep breathing! It may sound an extraneous remark, but breathing is important for us. Not just the reflex action that pumps oxygen into our bodies, but good breathing that eases tensions and promotes calmness, and has a very positive effect on our body's functions. When we are stressed or anxious we breathe more rapidly, using only the upper part of our chest. Chest breathing offers the quickest boost of oxygen to the body system, but in the long run it is not effective. When we are tired and depressed we breathe more deeply, exhaling or sighing.

Although chest breathing is natural and involuntary for most of us, it is really a part of the fight or flight syndrome, aroused when the organism is challenged by some external stress or danger. Because of the reciprocity between breath and mind, chest breathing in turn gives rise to tension and anxiety.

When breathing from the chest the lower lobes of the lungs, which receive an abundant supply of blood, are not adequately ventilated. Consequently the gas exchange that takes place between the air in the lungs and the blood is inadequate. Waste product starts to build up in the lungs, leading to increasingly less efficient breathing and a feeling of tiredness and lethargy.

Breathing clean air is essential as it oxygenates the blood and makes the tissues function more efficiently. Air is also believed to have antiseptic properties. But breathing on its own is not enough: how to breathe is also vitally important. The correct way to breathe is by contracting and relaxing the diaphragm, forcing the flow of air in and out of the lungs, allowing them to inflate and empty completely.

In turn, the body is able to work more effectively since it has a good supply of oxygen. You may actually find that diaphragmatic breathing needs to be relearned. Try it when you are stressed or tired. Lying comfortably on the floor with eyes closed, place your hands just below your rib cage and breath slowly. Feel your hands rising, then breathe out and feel them fall. Do this regularly, especially when under stress, until it becomes natural for you.

At Chiva-Som we have an oxygen power fitness programme that involves the inhalation of oxygen enhanced with an intake of vitamins and minerals. It is conducted under the supervision of a medical consultant. Other spas and fitness centres around the world also offer this form of treatment, so you might consider seeking out a qualified practitioner. Our own programme is designed for use by men and women of all ages, and at all levels of fitness.

During 20 minutes of cardiovascular exercise, the heart rate will be controlled while the body absorbs the oxygen, thus reducing the lactic acid accumulation in the muscles. It also involves improvement of cellular functioning such as repairing and building tissues, energy storage, and metabolism. The programme will help to improve endurance and stamina, and gives a general feeling of wellbeing to body and mind.

MAINTAINING THE BODY'S FRAMEWORK

Many of us slouch, stand badly, or sit incorrectly. We spend too long each day at a desk, in front of a computer, or doing something else that evolution has yet to catch up with. Being overweight also does not help the body's posture. Your skeleton was designed to carry a certain amount of weight, and if you overload it, the frame of your body will bend and buckle.

Good posture means maintaining the natural curve of the spine. Not only should the correct posture be used when standing or sitting, it should also be incorporated into all activities, thereby minimising the amount of harmful stress the spine and consequently the skeleton and muscle system must bear. The spine is central to the body and also to the autonomic nervous system.

Consequently poor posture will imbalance the body's mechanisms, twisting the muscles along the spine, causing circulation blockages and misalignment of the neuro-transmitters. Very often painful conditions of the spine and extremities can originate in areas of high stress, precipitated by musculo-skeletal imbalances.

Early warning signs of postural problems may include the inability to sit or stand for prolonged periods of time, stiffness when rising from a chair, or a feeling of exhaustion at the end of the day. Failure to correct these early warning signs often leads to muscle imbalance, loss of normal flexibility, and often a feeling of discomfort that appears to have arisen for no apparent reason.

The simplest way to keep good posture is to hold the shoulders slightly back and try to keep your shoulder blades as close together as you can. Tuck your chin and your tummy in. But then, many of us will have gone past the stage where correcting our posture is that easy. We need a little guidance. The happy news is that with the appropriate treatment, correction is relatively easy.

Equilibropathy is one system of therapy that has been proven to effectively help balance the body structure, clear the mind and boost the spirit. How it works is very interesting and easy to understand in terms of modern scientific logic, through the principles of anatomy and physiology. An examination by a specialist of your spinal column and associated muscles, by look and touch, will help determine the causes and effects of your problems. Acupuncture will relax the abnormally tense muscles and release the blockages, thus allowing improvement in circulation and nerve signal transmission in the body.

Specially designed exercises are taught during an equilibropathy session. Hence, the body structure will become more balanced, and the mind clearer. This will also work wonders for the spirit. Maintenance of the proper posture as instructed and physically corrected during the treatment will prevent the body from becoming further out of balance, while regular practice of the exercises will continuously improve your general health and the natural healing process.

HYPNOTISED TO HEALTH

Hypnosis is yet another area that has become associated with extreme ideas or even trickery, but it is a genuine enough therapy and of course is probably as old as the human race. These days we use the word "hypnotherapy", and it is the process of putting a subject in a state similar to deep sleep yet able to respond to external suggestion.

Hypnotherapy encompasses a holistic approach to health that includes a person's mental and physical wellbeing. In practice, it is a dramatic rapid intervention system which reshapes the subject's feelings of competence and capability. Within a hypnotherapy session, one may discover hidden memories, latent creativity, new insights, a feeling of competence, and release of fear. Deep emotions may be touched. It is a very profound experience.

A course of hypnotherapy can be used in a variety of cases, including weight control, stress, phobias and fears, memory improvement, self-image enhancement, insomnia, giving up smoking, skills enhancement, and building energy. Importantly, in hypnotherapy one can come to the realisation that we are responsible for our own realities and can choose to change or recreate our perceptions and beliefs, not merely accepting what we believe we must accept. This "consciousness of self" or a wakening of awareness is one of the highest rewards of hypnotherapy.

The most important thing a hypnotherapist can teach the subject during the pre-induction, induction, therapy and programming phases is that the subconscious mind can be trusted and relied upon completely.

One way in which the hypnotherapist works is to create a positive present by recreating the past. Our present experience is influenced by past memories contained in our subconscious minds. When we change our current attitudes, it influences our beliefs and motivations toward our present reality. So we can manifest a creative and successful present and future by re-educating the past stored in our subconscious minds. As a child, we are influenced by the beliefs and conditioning we receive from our parents and environment. As adults, we can re-educate or re-write our past scripts and the roles being played in the present.

This is why, after hypnotherapy, the subject can learn to look at things that are unpleasant without fear: he or she will have a willingness to understand and cope with a new direction. Re-education through hypnotherapy is a complex restructuring of subjective experiences that can be initiated very simply and then gently guided toward a therapeutic goal. It can enable you to learn to trust, to communicate and to use that vast range of hidden resources stored within your own subconscious mind.

Hypnosis is one of the most valuable tools in the world today for the enrichment of lives. With hypnosis, undesirable habits can be eliminated, desirable habits can be created or enforced, human problems can be dealt with constructively and resolved, and true happiness can be instilled to replace unhappiness.

A HOME FOR THE MIND

Few appreciate the fact that our mind exists and needs a home, a place where it feels secure, relaxed and happy. Taken for granted, the poor mind goes looking for its own home alone. For you, this gives rise to endless perplexing desires. A home can be created for your mind by focusing it on a single selected object or activity. This is known as mind training, and there are two ways of doing it: formal mind training, and mind training in action.

Formal mind training is when you arrange a place and time to practise formally. There are five methods of practice:
Sitting
Standing
Walking
Lying down
Loving kindness

Mind training in action is when you keep your mind totally focused on whatever you are doing at a particular moment: this can be an everyday activity such as eating, washing, or working.
There are two phases in mind training, namely:
Samatha bhavana, or tranquil mind training
Vipassana bhavana, or insight mind training

To calm the mind down by any technique is called tranquil mind training. When the mind is calm, relaxed, serene, and totally focused on a single object, it is concentrated. We must practise this well enough until the mind becomes fully tamed and obeys orders, just like a car that can be driven or parked anywhere. The tamed mind is good for any kind of work.

To get this tamed mind to function in the most beneficial way, that is to see, observe, examine, or experience things the way they actually are, is called insight mind training. For spiritual achievement, the tamed mind is used to learn and appreciate that all things change. Once the mind realises this it will not cling or attach anymore. With a well-trained mind, a blissful life can be accomplished.

Here is how to train your mind formally.

SITTING

- Look for a serene place.
- Sit in a comfortable posture.
- Do short breathing: breathe slow, deep, long, for about three minutes. Always keep your mind on your breathing by either following it in and out, or finding a point in the nostril where the breath can best be felt. Use this as a checkpoint. Feel the air as it rushes through to the point. Keep the mind there, direct all of your attention there all the time. If the mind creeps away, fetch it back and try again. After three minutes return the breath back to normal. Breathe naturally.
- Follow this with normal breathing, that is, by finding the most comfortable length of breath, and breathing normally. Continue breathing like this for 30 minutes. Keep the mind always on the breath. Since this kind of breathing is fine and delicate, it is harder to focus on. So we have to be very cautious and watchful, otherwise the mind will slip away.

STANDING

- Stand up and relax every part of your body.
- Focus your mind on the sensation of the floor underneath your feet.
- Repeat the breathing as for the sitting posture.

WALKING

- Select a path 10 metres long.
- Walk back and forth slowly while focusing the mind on the sensation of the ground under your feet, for 30 minutes.

LYING DOWN

- Lie flat on your back on the floor and relax every part of your body.
- Focus your mind on the sensation of the floor underneath your back.
- Repeat the breathing as for the sitting or standing postures.

CRANIOSACRAL THERAPY

A treatment that is fast gaining popularity is craniosacral therapy. Very much a hands-on technique, this extremely gentle therapy "listens", via the hands, to what is going on in your body, and in this way both identifies and relieves pains and tensions.

Craniosacral therapy is based on a number of findings about the body's subtle physiology, which were made by osteopaths in the USA nearly 100 years ago. These findings show that every cell in a healthy body expresses a rhythmic movement fundamental to life, called craniosacral motion. At the core of the body the cerebrospinal fluid, which bathes and cushions the brain and spinal cord, expresses this motion in a tide-like ebb and flow.

Throughout our lives, our bodies have been subject to physical knocks or emotional stress causing the body's tissues to contract. Sometimes, when the shock is severe, the tissues stay contracted. This causes any stresses, strains, tensions or traumas "stored" in the body to restrict its functioning, leading to problems over the years. The effects could be physical, such as back pain, migraine or indigestion, or emotional, such as anxiety or depression.

Restrictions in the body's functioning show up in craniosacral motion. Craniosacral therapists are trained to feel this subtle motion in the body, and to identify areas of congestion or restriction. Then, using their hands, they reflect the body back to pattern and an easier mode of functioning.

THE R E C

I P E S

TABLE

The exact equivalents in the following tables have been rounded for convenience.

US/UK

oz	= ounce
lb	= pound
tbsp	= tablespoon
qt	= quart
tsp	= teaspoon

METRIC

gm	= gramme
kg	= kilogramme
mm	= millimetre
cm	= centimetre
ml	= millilitre
l	= litre

WEIGHTS

US/UK		Metric
1 oz		30 gm
2 oz		60 gm
3 oz		90 gm
4 oz	(1/4 lb)	125 gm
5 oz	(1/3 lb)	155 gm
6 oz		185 gm
7 oz		220 gm
8 oz	(1/2 lb)	250 gm
10 oz		315 gm
12 oz	(3/4 lb)	375 gm
14 oz		440 gm
16 oz	(1 lb)	500 gm
11/2 lb		750 gm
2 lb		1 kg

OVEN TEMPERATURES

Fahrenheit	Celsius	Gas
250	120	1/2
275	140	1
300	150	2
325	160	3
350	180	4
375	190	5
400	200	6
425	220	7
450	230	8
475	240	9
500	260	10

# of EQUI

VALENTS

LIQUIDS

US	Metric	UK
2 tbsp	30 ml	1 fl oz
1/4 cup	60 ml	2 fl oz
1/3 cup	80 ml	3 fl oz
1/2 cup	125 ml	4 fl oz
2/3 cup	160 ml	5 fl oz
3/4 cup	180 ml	6 fl oz
1 cup	250 ml	8 fl oz
1 1/2 cup	375 ml	12 fl oz
2 cups	500 ml	16 fl oz
4 cups/1 qt	1 l	32 fl oz

EQUIVALENTS FOR COMMONLY USED INGREDIENTS

All-purpose (plain) flour / dried bread crumbs / chopped nuts

1/4 cup	1 oz	30 gm
1/3 cup	1 1/2 oz	45 gm
1/2 cup	2 oz	60 gm
3/4 cup	3 oz	90 gm
1 cup	4 oz	125 gm
1 1/2 cup	6 oz	185 gm
2 cups	8 oz	250 gm

Wholewheat (wholemeal) flour

3 tbsp	1 oz	30 gm
1/2 cup	2 oz	60 gm
2/3 cup	3 oz	90 gm
1 cup	4 oz	125 gm
1 1/4 cups	5 oz	155 gm
1 2/3 cups	7 oz	210 gm
1 3/4 cups	8 oz	250 gm

Brown sugar

1/4 cup	1 1/2 oz	45 gm
1/2 cup	3 oz	90 gm
3/4 cup	4 oz	125 gm
1 cup	5 1/2 oz	170 gm
1 1/2 cups	8 oz	250 gm
2 cups	10 oz	315 gm

White sugar

1/4 cup	2 oz	60 gm
1/3 cup	3 oz	90 gm
1/2 cup	4 oz	125 gm
3/4 cup	6 oz	185 gm
1 cup	8 oz	250 gm
1 1/2 cups	12 oz	375 gm
2 cups	1 lb	500 gm

Long-grain rice / cornmeal

1/3 cup	2 oz	60 gm
1/2 cup	2 1/2 oz	75 gm
3/4 cup	4 oz	125 gm
1 cup	5 oz	155 gm
1 1/2 cups	8 oz	250 gm

Dried beans

1/4 cup	1 1/2 oz	45 gm
1/3 cup	2 oz	60 gm
1/2 cup	3 oz	90 gm
3/4 cup	5 oz	155 gm
1 cup	6 oz	185 gm
1 1/4 cups	8 oz	250 gm
1 1/2 cups	12 oz	375 gm

Grated Parmesan / Romano cheese

1/4 cup	1 oz	30 gm
1/2 cup	2 oz	60 gm
3/4 cup	3 oz	90 gm
1 cup	4 oz	125 gm
1 1/3 cups	5 oz	155 gm
2 cups	7 oz	220 gm

HERBS &

BASIL, THAI SWEET
A mild anise-flavoured basil with reddish-coloured stems, used for its aromatic qualities. Cannot be substituted by Italian basil. Available from good Asian vegetable stockists. Fresh leaves can be chewed as a breath freshener.

CHILLI (PRIK CHEE FAH)
Growing 9-12 cm in length, and either yellow, red or green. Not as hot as the bird chilli. There is no discernable difference between the colours.

SOY SAUCE, LIGHT (SOYA SAUCE)
A light, clear, brown, salty liquid made from fermentation of soya beans mixed with roasted wheat. Used as a seasoning, this can be substituted with Asian nam pla or fish sauce. For those with gluten intolerance, a non-wheat variety called tamari is available.

SPICES used in Thai cooking

CORIANDER, FRESH (CHINESE PARSLEY, CILANTRO)

Claimed to be the world's most commonly-used herb, the leaves are often chosen for decoration, with stem and roots for seasoning. Heavily used in Asian kitchens, the Thai kitchen is the only one to use the roots as well. Available from good Asian food stockists. Seeds cannot be substituted for fresh leaves. If you cannot find fresh coriander, try growing your own, or substitute with flat leaf parsley or chervil.

SHALLOT (HOM DAENG)

These small, zesty, Thai red onions are sweet and aromatic. An essential ingredient in many Thai dishes because of their taste and appearance, they can be substituted with European shallots, small red onions or small brown onions without detriment in most cases, but the water content of the onions is much higher.

LEMONGRASS

Closely related to citronella, this hard grass grows rapidly in almost any soil. The base of 10-12 cm length of the plant is used, with the green leafy part discarded. Young tender lemongrass stalks can be finely chopped and eaten, but older stalks should be cut into 3-5 cm lengths and bruised before being added only as a flavouring agent. Can be substituted with virtually any other strong lemon-flavoured herb if not available. Lemongrass oil will sooth an upset stomach and indigestion.

BEAN, SOY (SOYA BEAN)

Available in both white, red and black varieties, but the white is the most common. Excellent source of vegetable protein. Must be soaked overnight, and takes about 2 1/2 hours to cook.

BEAN, BLACK (BLACK KIDNEY BEAN):

Exceptionally rich in dietary fibre, this bean needs to be soaked overnight before cooking.

BEAN, HARICOT (NAVY BEAN, PEA BEAN)

The bean from which baked beans are made. Excellent source of vegetable protein and dietary fibre. Needs to be soaked overnight before cooking.

BEAN, KIDNEY (RED KIDNEY BEAN)

Used in both sweet and savoury cooking. Excellent source of vegetable protein and dietary fibre. Needs to be soaked overnight before cooking.

CHICK PEA (GARBANZO BEAN, BENGAL GRAM, DESI CHICKPEA)

Good source of vegetable protein and dietary fibre, and unlike most beans contains a small amount of oil. Soak overnight before cooking.

CINNAMON (OB CHUEY)

From the bark of a tree, the type of cinnamon used in Thailand is of only one kind, that from the Cassia tree. It is used in meat dishes and curries.

CHILLI, BIRD (PRIK KHEE NOO)

The smallest of the chillies, but also the hottest. Take care when chopping them, and do not rub your eyes. Chillies stimulate blood circulation and are reputed to help prevent heart disease and cancer.

CUMIN (YEE RAA)

Seeds look like caraway and fennel, but taste quite different. Only cumin is used in Thai cooking, not the other two, and it is used in making curry pastes.

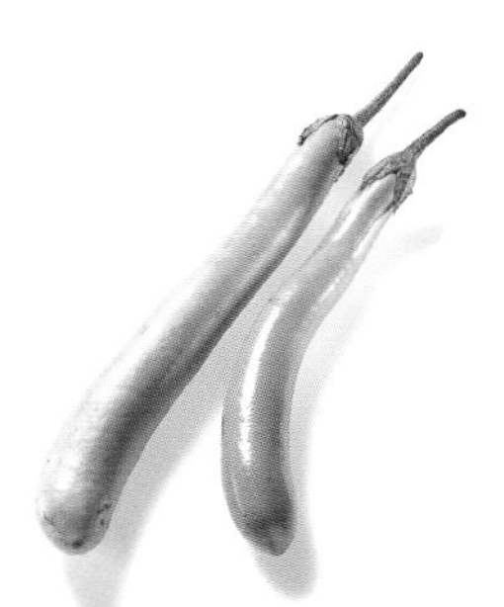

EGGPLANT, GREEN (MA KHUE YAO)

The long, Thai eggplant is a much "wetter" variety of eggplant than the European purple aubergine or eggplant, but can be substituted with care in nearly all cases. Slender and long (approximately 20 cm) it is also available in white, yellow and purple. However, the green variety is by far the most common.

EGGPLANT, PEA (MA KHUE PHUANG)

Grows in small clusters, and looks like green peas. Has a crisp texture and slightly bitter taste. Is often used in Thai curries. If unable to purchase from your Asian food stockist, diced green apple if added at the end of the cooking will give you a similar texture, or just omit from the recipe.

EGGPLANT, WHITE (MA KHUE PROH)

Sometimes called crisp eggplant. Believed to aid digestion and blood circulation. One of the essential ingredients of Thai curries. Always choose crisp, firm-fleshed ones to ensure freshness, and use within a few days of purchase or they become bitter. If unable to find, you can substitute other aubergines, but the end texture will not be the same.

FLAX SEED (LINSEED)

Small, brown, shiny seeds, used to produce linseed oil. The richest food source of alpha linolenic acid (of the omega 3 fatty acid family). Linolenic acid is a polyunsaturated fatty acid, with claims of assisting in everything from blood clotting to allergies and cholesterol, and is important in our diets.

GALANGAL (KHA)

Resembling an upturned claw, this member of the ginger family is a pale pink rhizome with a subtle citrus flavour. It can be very tough and is not normally eaten, but is usually added in large pieces to impart flavour. Fresh young ginger can be substituted, but you will not end up with the same flavour.

GARLIC (KRATIAM)

Thailand is literally overflowing with garlic plants. Whole cloves, smashed garlic and garlic oil are used in almost every Thai dish.

GINGER, FRESH (KHING)

Resembling a flat hand, ginger has over 400 members included in its family. Always choose young fresh ginger if available. Easily grated, it is eaten raw or cooked and is used widely in many Asian cuisines. Ginger is acknowledged to improve digestion and to counteract nausea and vomiting. Powdered ginger is not a substitute for fresh ginger.

GUAVA (FARANG)

Similar in size to a large green apple, there is also a smaller, pink-fleshed variety. In Thailand it is always eaten green, and is often dipped in a salt, sugar and chilli mix as a refreshing snack. The edible thin skin and slightly sweet, crisp flesh can be added to salads, pickled or freshly juiced. A good source of vitamins A and C, the leaves can be boiled and the liquid used as a breath-freshener.

KAFFIR LIME LEAF

From the kaffir lime, which has virtually no juice, these fleshy green and glossy leaves resemble a figure eight. Imparting a unique flavour, they can be finely shredded and added to salads, or torn and added to soups and curries. Can be substituted with other lemon-flavoured herbs, but the best option is to freeze the leaves when you can find them, as they retain all their flavour and texture on thawing.

LEMON, THAI (KALAMANSI LIME)

Lemons when referred to in any Thai recipe always mean the thin-skinned green kalamansi limes. An excellent source of vitamin C, they are used to enhance the flavour of chilli-hot condiments, as well as create some very special salads and desserts.

MISO

This Japanese delicacy is commonly available in white, yellow and red varieties, but is essentially cooked soybeans mixed with other grains, mould and salt, then aged for anything up to several years. Purported to have amazing health benefits, it is used for everything from a thickener for a sauce, to a salad dressing, soup flavouring or fish seasoning. Can contain from 5-18 percent salt, so should be used sparingly.

MUSHROOM, OYSTER (TREE MUSHROOM, PEUROTTE)

Today most are cultivated, but in the wild they can be found growing on trees. Generally a soft oyster-grey in colour, the yellow variety is occasionally seen. Due to their high water content, they will shrink to only 50 percent of original size on cooking. Nearly always stir-fried or braised, they can be eaten raw.

MUSHROOM, SHIITAKE (BLACK FOREST MUSHROOM, CHINESE MUSHROOM)

Widely available either fresh or dried. The dried ones should be soaked in warm water for 15 minutes to soften. They do not need peeling, but the stems should be discarded as they are very tough. Strong in flavour, they should be used either sparingly or in strong-flavour dishes only.

MUSHROOM, STRAW

This mushroom looks nothing like straw, but gets its name from the rice straw in which it is grown. The mushrooms are extremely perishable, hence it is very rare to find them available fresh. Unfortunately the canned straw mushrooms often used as a substitute do not have the delicate flavour nor the firm texture of fresh straw mushrooms.

NOODLES, EGG (BA MEE)

These yellow egg noodles are similar to spaghetti as they are made from the same ingredients. Available fresh from good Asian food stockists and larger supermarkets, they can also be purchased in the dried form.

NOODLES, GLASS (VERMICELLI, WOON SEN)

These fine, hard and transparent noodles are made from mung beans. They must be soaked in cold or warm water for a few minutes before cooking, when they will become transparent.

NOODLES, RICE

A staple of the Asian diet, these large, flat, white noodle sheets are cut into strips of differing width to provide wide, narrow or thin noodles. Available fresh from good Asian food stockists, these may also be purchased in a dried form. Dried noodles should be soaked before cooking.

NORI (KEEM, TSU TS-AI)

A variety of seaweed, nori is generally available in its compressed dried form, but can occasionally be purchased fresh. Toasting the sheets quickly over an open flame for a few seconds prior to using will enhance the flavour. Used in sheets to wrap sushi, or shredded and used as a garnish or condiment. Seaweed is an excellent source of calcium and a good source of many minerals including zinc, selenium and cobalt. One teaspoon of seaweed contains 15 times the recommended daily amount of iodine. Store in an airtight container.

OKRA (LADIES FINGERS, BENDI)

Long, green pods similar in size to ladies fingers, this unusual vegetable may be covered with a fine downy hair. Containing many edible seeds and a white mucilaginous substance, it is not to everyone's taste. Always choose the youngest crisp pods. Leaving the pods whole in cooking avoids the stickiness, or slice thinly and use to thicken soups and stews.

ORANGE, THAI (SOM)

These are a green-skinned variety of fruit, not dissimilar to mandarins or tangerines. Hence the juice is much sweeter than from the navel or Valencia oranges of Europe. They contain large seeds, but the bright orange flesh is very juicy.

PEPPER (PRIK-THAI)

Black, white and green peppercorn types. Black is milder and more aromatic than white. Green peppercorns have a special taste all their own. Used as flavouring.

ROSE APPLE (WATER APPLE)

A member of the myrtle family, these delicious, bell-shaped fruits are available in either delicate green or red varieties. Waxy to look at, the crisp outer part has a soft, spongy pith with one or two seeds. With no discernable flavour and only a slight sweetness at the height of the season, they are prized more for their juiciness. The whole fruit (except the seeds) is eaten.

SESAME (NGA)

Identical to sesame seeds the world over. In Thai cooking sesame seeds are used for oil and for flavouring. The seeds are white with black shells. Black sesame seeds are also available.

SOY SAUCE, DARK

This is a sweeter, viscous liquid made by mixing soy sauce with molasses. Used more as a dipping sauce. It should not be confused with Japanese soy sauce, which has a distinct "brewed" aroma.

TOFU, FIRM

There are many types of tofu, from smooth silken ones to dried and fermented varieties (tempeh), and even some that contain egg. Firm tofu has been drained of much of the whey, and is an excellent protein and calcium source of nutrition that can be stir-fried, or even used as a substitute for soft cheeses.

TURMERIC (KHAMIN)

Bright orange roots used for the colouring in yellow curries. White turmeric, a different type, is used as a raw vegetable and resembles ginger.

WASABI POWDER (JAPANESE HORSERADISH)

This naturally green powder is made from the roots of a native plant that grows in the mountain streams of Japan. Add a few drops of water to make a thick, fiery paste that enhances the subtle flavours of raw fish.

WATER CHESTNUT (HAEW)

Grown in swampy grounds, they have a crisp, white flesh when peeled. Can be eaten raw or cooked. A good source of vitamin C and dietary fibre, they are rarely available as fresh outside of Asia. Canned Chinese water chestnuts available from any Asian food stockist are a good substitute, as is fresh Mexican jicoma.

clockwise from left
Cranberry and guava juice
Five-vegetable juice
Green fruit cocktail
Cleansing cocktail
Soy milk

1 Breakfast

Cranberry and Guava Juice
Serves: 1 Calories: 56 Fat: 0.6 gm

- 2 large green guavas
- $^{3}/_{4}$ cup high-bush cranberries
- $^{1}/_{2}$ cup ice cubes

Cut the guavas into small pieces and process in a food juicer. Pour the juice into a food blender with the ice and the cranberries. Process until smooth. Serve immediately so the juice does not oxidise.

Five-vegetable Juice
Serves: 1 Calories: 109 Fat: 1.1 gm

- 2 medium red tomatoes
- 1 clove garlic
- 5 small cucumbers
- 1 red bell pepper
- 1 tsp lime juice

Wash all the ingredients well. Prepare the juicer and process all the ingredients together. Serve immediately.

For cold juice, chill the vegetables well before making the juice. Drink immediately for maximum benefit from this natural "vitamin pill".

Green Fruit Cocktail

Serves: 1 Calories: 85 Fat: 0.7 gm

- 200 gm green apples
- 2 kiwi fruits
- 1 cup green grapes
- 160 gm rose apples or other green fruits
- 1/2 cup crushed ice

Wash the fruits carefully, ensuring that all the dirt is removed. Remove the seeds from the apples and the skin from the kiwi fruits. For the other fruits, leave the skin on.

Process the apples, grapes and rose apples in a juicer. Then pour into a food blender with the kiwis and the ice. Process until smooth and serve.

Cleansing Cocktail

Serves: 1 Calories: 125 Fat: 0.1 gm

- 1/2 cucumber
- 1 carrot
- 1/2 beetroot
- 1/2 apple
- 1 tsp fresh ginger, grated
- 1/2 cup water

Remove the seeds from the apple, but leave the skin on. Pass the apple, cucumber, beetroot, carrot and grated ginger through a juicer.

Add the water and serve.

Ideal for clearing age or liver spots.

Soy Milk

Serves: 10 Calories: 90 Fat: 2 gm

- 200 gm soybeans, dry
- water for soaking
- water for processing
- 1.5 litres water for boiling

In a large bowl, cover the beans with double its volume of water and soak overnight in the refrigerator.

Next day, drain and rinse the beans thoroughly. Place equal quantities of drained beans and water in a food processor and blend to a smooth and creamy consistency. This mixture is called go.

In a very large pot, bring 1.5 litres of water to the boil, and add the go mix. Over a high heat bring back to the boil, stirring continuously to ensure that the mixture does not burn.

When the mixture boils up to the top of the pot, sprinkle a little cold water over it to cool it down slightly.

Bring back to the boil and repeat the process another two times. This is to ensure that any toxins in the bean skins are destroyed.

Strain through a fine muslin cloth into a bowl before serving in individual glasses.

The liquid is called soy or soya milk and the solid bean that is left is called okara or soya bran. The okara can be used as a nutritious substitute for rice in dishes such as vegetarian fried "rice".

Morning Scones

Serves: 12 Calories: 95 Fat: 0.4 gm

- 1 cup plain flour
- 1/2 tsp baking soda
- 1 cup wholewheat flour
- 2 tsp baking powder
- 1/3 cup dark raisins
- 1 cup apple puree
- 1/3 cup skim milk

Sift the plain flour with the baking soda and baking powder. Add the wholewheat flour and raisins. Gently mix through, incorporating as much air as possible. Add the apple puree and just enough of the milk to form a stiff dough.

On a lightly-floured surface and with a minimum of kneading, form the dough into a ball. Gently roll out the dough until 2 cm thick. Using a sharp cutter or knife cut into 12 pieces. For a more traditional scone, cut into 4 cm round pieces.

Place on a non-stick baking sheet, leaving at least 2 cm between each piece. Brush the tops lightly with skim milk.

Bake at 190C for 16-18 minutes, or until lightly browned. Transfer to a serving plate, and serve hot. Best served straight from the oven.

Morning scones

Apple sauce muffins

Chiva-Som Muesli
Serves: 4 Calories: 275 Fat: 6.5 gm

- 3 cups low-fat yoghurt
- 4 tbsp oatmeal
- 4 tbsp raisins
- 1 tsp walnuts, lightly roasted and chopped
- 1 tsp almonds, lightly roasted and chopped
- 1 tbsp honey
- 2 green apples

Wash the apples thoroughly, and leaving the skin on, cut into matchsticks. Place into a bowl with the oatmeal, raisins, honey and chopped nuts. Fold through the yoghurt. Place in the refrigerator for at least 5-10 minutes so that the oatmeal softens a little and the flavours combine. Serve.

If preferred, the oatmeal can be pre-soaked in water, but ensure that it is well drained before adding to the rest of the ingredients.

Apple Sauce Muffins
Serves: 12 Calories: 130 Fat: 0.6 gm

- 2 cups wholewheat flour
- 1 tbsp baking powder
- 300 ml apple puree
- 125 ml apple concentrate
- 2 egg whites, beaten
- 1/2 cup dark raisins

Preheat oven. In a large mixing bowl, combine the flour and baking powder. Mix well. Add the apple puree, apple con-centrate and lightly beaten egg whites. Mix until just moist-ened. Add the raisins and fold in carefully.

Spoon into non-stick muffin cups until three-quarters full and bake at 170C for 16-18 minutes. Remove from the oven when a wooden toothpick inserted into the centre of a muffin comes out clean. Leave to sit for 5 minutes before turning out. Serve warm or at room temperature.

Pineapple Bran Muffins
Serves: 12 Calories: 106 Fat: 0.6 gm

- 1 1/4 cups skim milk
- 1 1/2 cups oat bran
- 1/2 cup apple concentrate
- 2 1/2 cups wholewheat flour
- 1 tbsp baking powder
- 240 gm pineapple, chopped with juice
- 2 egg whites

Mix the milk, bran and apple concentrate, and set aside for 15 minutes. Combine the flour and baking powder, and stir to mix well. Add the bran mixture, the pineapple with juice and the egg whites, and stir just until the dry ingredients are moistened.

Spoon into muffin cups and to bake, follow the instructions as for Apple Sauce Muffins.

Chocolate crumb muffins

Chocolate Crumb Muffins

Serves: 12 Calories: 150 Fat: 1.4 gm

- 1 cup wholewheat flour
- 1 cup oat flour
- 1/4 cup plus 2 tbsp cocoa powder
- 1/2 cup light brown sugar
- 1 tbsp baking powder
- 3 pears, poached
- 2 egg whites
- 1/2 vanilla pod

Topping

- 1/2 cup plus 2 tbsp quick-cooking oats
- 1 tbsp cocoa powder
- 1-2 tbsp honey

In a large bowl combine the flours, cocoa, brown sugar and baking powder, and stir to mix well. Place the poached pears with the poaching liquid in a blender and puree until smooth. Add 1 1/2 cups of this mixture to the flour mixture. (Keep the remaining puree for use in other recipes.)

Add the beaten egg whites and vanilla seeds from the pod, and stir through carefully until all the dry ingredients are moistened.

To make the topping, combine the oats, cocoa and honey and stir until the mixture is moist and crumbly. Set aside.

Spoon the muffin mix into muffin cups and fill three-quar-- ters full with the batter. Sprinkle a rounded teaspoonful of the topping over each muffin and press very lightly into the batter.

Bake at 170C for 15 minutes and follow the instructions as for the Apple Sauce Muffins.

Strawberry Streusel Muffins

Serves: 10 Calories: 140 Fat: 0.9 gm

- 1 1/2 cups wholewheat flour
- 1/2 cup oat flour
- 1/3 cup sugar
- 1 tbsp baking powder
- 2 cups strawberries, pureed
- 1/2 cup plus 2 tbsp orange juice
- 2 egg whites

Topping

- 1/2 cup quick-cooking oats
- 1 tbsp wholewheat flour
- 1 tbsp apple concentrate
- 10 whole strawberries
- 1 tbsp orange juice

Combine the flours and baking powder and stir to mix well. Add the pureed strawberries and orange juice, and stir just until the dry ingredients are moistened. Whip the egg whites with the sugar to a stiff peak and fold through the mixture.

To make the topping, stir the ingredients together until moist and crumbly. Spoon the muffin mix into muffin cups, filling three-quarters full with the batter. Push a whole strawberry into the centre of each muffin. Sprinkle the topping over each muffin.

Bake at 170C for 15 minutes and follow the instructions as for the Chocolate Crumb Muffins.

Egg white frittata

Buckwheat Pancake with Strawberries

Serves: 6 Calories: 115 Fat: 0.6 gm

- 1 cup wholewheat flour
- 1/2 cup buckwheat flour
- 1 1/2 tsp baking powder
- 1/2 cup apple concentrate
- 2 egg whites, beaten
- 1 1/4 - 1 1/2 cups skim milk
- 50 gm strawberries

Cut the strawberries in half and place in a small pot with half of the apple concentrate. Heat through until the strawberries are hot. Remove from the heat and cool.

In a large bowl, sift the wholewheat flour and baking powder together. Add the buckwheat flour. In a separate bowl, mix the lightly beaten egg whites, the remaining half of the apple concentrate and all the skim milk together. Stir into the dry ingredients. Mix well to incorporate but do not over-mix. Add a little more milk if the mixture is too dry, depending on the origin of the flours used.

Heat a non-stick skillet or griddle over a medium heat. Spoon in a little of the pancake mixture and roll the pan so that the mix is evenly distributed over the pan. When the pancake curls a little at the edges, it is ready to turn.

Use a spatula to assist flipping the pancake and cook for a further 30 seconds. Turn out and repeat the process until all the pancakes are cooked.

Spoon the cooked strawberries over the pancakes and serve.

Egg White Frittata

Serves: 6 Calories: 135 Fat: 0.9 gm

- 16 egg whites
- 1/2 onion, thinly sliced
- 1/2 cup green bell pepper, cubed
- 1/2 cup red bell pepper, cubed
- 1/2 cup spinach, chopped
- 15 mushrooms, sliced
- 1/2 bunch basil
- 5 medium tomatoes
- 30 gm spring onions
- black pepper

In a non-stick pan, "sautee" the onion and bell peppers with a little water until softened. Add the spinach and the mush-rooms. Cook briefly, then add the fresh basil. Season to taste with black pepper. Cool completely.

Lightly beat the egg whites and mix with the spinach mix. Heat a small non-stick skillet and pour in the mix as when making a very thick pancake. Cook over medium heat until the mixture is set. Then with extreme care, flip the frittata to cook the other side. Alternatively, place the pan under a grill to cook the top of the frittata.

Vegetarian Miso Soup

Serves: 4 Calories: 70 Fat: 0.7 gm

- 1 1/2 tbsp miso paste
- 600 ml vegetable stock
- 1 small carrot
- 1 small daikon white radish
- 8 pieces fresh shiitake mushrooms
- 50 gm firm tofu
- 2 spring onions

Combine the miso paste with the vegetable stock and heat through. Add the whole shiitake mushrooms and simmer. Finely shred the carrot and white radish.

Cut the tofu into 1 cm cubes and add with the vegetables to the simmering soup base and cook for 1-2 minutes only.

Finely shred the spring onions using equal quantities of the green leaf and white bulb. Place in the serving bowls.

Pour the soup over the spring onions in the serving bowls and serve.

The miso paste is salty, so no additional seasoning is re-quired.

Miso – vegetables and seafood

Seafood Miso Soup

Serves: 4 Calories: 90 Fat: 1.2 gm

- 1 1/2 tbsp miso paste
- 600 ml vegetable stock
- 1 small carrot
- 1 small daikon white radish
- 4 pieces fresh shiitake mushrooms
- 120 gm prawn tails, peeled
- 120 gm snapper fillet, diced
- 50 gm firm tofu
- 2 spring onions

Prepare as for the Vegetarian Miso Soup but add the prawn tails and snapper with the vegetables to the simmering soup base and cook for 2 to 3 minutes. Serve as for the Vegeta-rian Miso Soup.

Thai noodle rolls

Appetisers

Thai Noodle Rolls

Serves: 8 Calories: 155 Fat: 2.8 gm

- 1 carrot
- 1/4 small cabbage
- 1 cup large beansprouts
- 250 gm enoki mushrooms
- 4 spring onions
- 2 bunches coriander
- 2 stalks Chinese celery
- 1 tsp sesame seeds
- 1/4 tsp sesame oil
- 16 pcs fresh rice noodle squares

Sauce

- 6 cloves garlic
- 2 large fresh chillies
- 3 coriander roots
- 500 ml tamarind juice
- 3 tbsp soy sauce (or rice vinegar)
- 1 tbsp apple concentrate (or other sweeteners)
- 1 tsp cornstarch
- 4 tsp cold water

Soak the beansprouts in iced water. Finely shred the carrot, cabbage and spring onions. Trim the tips of the enoki mushrooms and discard the woody stalks. Cut the celery and coriander to the same length as the beansprouts. Drain the beansprouts and mix all the vegetables together with the sesame seeds and sesame oil. Season with a little soy sauce if desired.

Lay out the rice noodles and cut into squares of approximately 10 cm x 10 cm. Place a tablespoon of the vegetable mixture in the centre and roll up. Repeat the process until all the rice noodle squares are used. Place the rolls on a steaming tray and steam to cook.

To make the sauce, pulse blend the garlic, chilli and coriander root with sufficient tamarind juice to make a paste (not too smooth). Place in a saucepan with the remaining tamarind juice, soy sauce and apple concentrate. Bring to the boil and simmer for 4-5 minutes. Mix the cornstarch with the cold water and add to the sauce to thicken slightly. Set aside to cool. Serve the cooked noodle rolls with the sauce.

Steamed prawn dumplings

Steamed Prawn Dumplings

Makes: 16 Calories: 50 Fat: 0.2 gm

- 450 gm prawn tails
- 2 dried shiitake mushrooms, soaked
- 2 water chestnuts
- 20 gm bamboo shoots
- 2 spring onions
- 2 tsp light soy sauce
- 1/4 tsp sesame oil
- 16 pcs wonton wrappers
- pepper
- egg white

Shell and de-vein the prawns. Finely chop the prawns, mushrooms, water chestnuts, spring onions and bamboo shoots. Mix all together. Season with soy sauce, sesame oil and pepper, adding to taste. Place a teaspoon of the mix on the centre of a wonton wrapper.

Moisten the edges with egg white and fold into a dumpling, crimping the edges.

Place in a steaming basket and repeat the process until all the wrappers have been used.

Steam dumplings for 7-10 minutes or until firm to the touch, and wrappers are translucent. Serve.

Open chicken ravioli

Open Chicken Ravioli

Serves: 6 Calories: 130 Fat: 2.0 gm

- 180 gm fresh wholewheat pasta
- 240 gm chicken breast, skinless
- 100 gm fresh oyster mushrooms
- 2 tomatoes
- 1 tsp fresh green peppercorns (or 1/4 tsp tinned)
- 50 gm fresh straw mushrooms (or button mushrooms)
- 1 tbsp soy sauce
- 1 large onion, shredded
- 1/3 cup soy milk
- 2 cloves garlic, crushed
- 1 tsp cornstarch
- 1/2 cup vegetable stock
- 2 litres water for boiling

Cut the chicken breast into thin medallions. Cut the tomatoes in half and remove the seeds. Shred the tomatoes. Cut the straw (or button) mushrooms in half and the oyster mushrooms into bite-size pieces.

In a saucepan place the onion and garlic with a little vegetable stock. Cook until softened, adding a little extra stock if it becomes too dry. Add the chicken and continue to cook. Add the tomatoes and mushrooms and mix well. Mix the cornstarch with the soy milk and add to the chicken. Bring to the boil and simmer until the cornstarch thickens the liq--

Lentil wontons with sweet and sour sauce, Thai style

uid. Season to taste with the soy sauce, and add the green peppercorns. If using tinned green peppercorns, wash three times before adding them.

Meanwhile on a lightly-floured board, roll the pasta out into sheets 2 mm thick. Cut into 12 pieces. Bring the water to a rolling boil and cook the pasta sheets until done. Drain. Place a piece of cooked pasta in the centre of a serving plate, spoon the chicken mix over and top with a second sheet of pasta. Serve.

Lentil Wontons with Sweet and Sour Sauce

Serves: 4 Calories: 150 Fat: 1.3 gm

- 1 cup lentils, cooked
- 2 tsp soy sauce
- 3 spring onions, finely chopped
- 1/2 tsp fresh ginger, grated
- 32 pcs wonton wrappers
- 2 litres of water for boiling

Sweet and sour sauce

- 1 cup vegetable stock
- 1/4 cup pineapple, diced
- 1/2 cucumber, seeded and diced
- 1/2 bell pepper, finely chopped
- 2 tomatoes, seeded and diced
- 2 tsp soy sauce
- 2 small chillies, finely chopped
- 1 tsp cornstarch
- 1 spring onion, finely chopped
- 3 tsp water

Lightly mash the lentils in a bowl, season with the soy sauce and add the spring onions and ginger. Place a teaspoon of the mix in the centre of a wonton wrapper. Moisten the edges of the wrapper and fold to seal. Place on a lightly-floured tray and cover to keep from drying out. Prepare each wonton in the same way.

To make the sauce, in a small saucepan bring the vegetable stock to the boil. Add the pineapple, cucumber, bell pep-- per and tomatoes. Simmer to heat through, then add the chillies and season to taste with the soy sauce. Mix the corn-starch with the water to a smooth sauce. The quantity re-quired will vary depending on the degree of ripeness of the vegetables used.

To cook the wontons, bring the water to a rolling boil and add the wontons. Cook for 3-4 minutes or until the wrap-pers are cooked and the lentil mix has heated through. Drain and place on serving dishes. Pour over the sauce and deco-rate with the chopped spring onions. Serve.

Snapper Sashimi Salad

Serves: 4 Calories: 130 Fat: 3.5 gm

- 400 gm fresh raw tuna or other fish of choice
- 2 spring onions
- 2 tbsp water
- 1 tbsp mustard powder
- 1 tbsp mirin
- 2 tbsp rice wine (sake)
- 3 tbsp rice vinegar
- 2 tbsp white miso paste
- 2 tbsp Japanese soy sauce
- 1/4 tsp wasabi powder (or as required)
- 1 tsp sesame seeds, toasted

Plunge the spring onions into boiling water for 5 seconds then into iced water to cool. Drain and pat dry. Set aside.

Mix the mustard with the water to a smooth paste. Let stand for a few minutes to develop the flavours. Meanwhile in a small pot, warm the sake and mirin together to burn off the alcohol. Add the miso paste, stirring constantly until it be--comes a thick paste. Place in a bowl with the mustard mix, rice vinegar, Japanese soy sauce and wasabi powder. Mix well and chill.

Before shredding the spring onions, plunge them into boiling water for 5 seconds, then iced water to cool. Cut the chilled and very fresh fish into small cubes and toss together with the miso mixture. Place on a serving plate and sprinkle with the green onions and sesame seeds.

Serve with salad leaves if desired.

Use only the freshest fish available for this dish.

Snapper sashimi salad

Steamed mushroom buns ***(page 76)***

Steamed Mushroom Buns

Serves: 16 Calories: 80 Fat: 0.8 gm

- 225 gm mushrooms, diced (fresh straw mushrooms for choice, but cultivated mushrooms or oyster mushrooms may be substituted)
- 30 ml vegetable stock
- 30 ml oyster sauce
- 3 spring onions, chopped
- 1 tbsp cornstarch
- 4 tbsp water (variable)
- black pepper

Dough
- 2 tbsp sugar
- 1 tbsp dried yeast
- 100 ml warm water
- 350 gm baker's flour
- 100 gm wholewheat flour
- 1/4 tsp salt

In a small saucepan, place the mushrooms with the vegetable stock. Cook over a medium heat until the mushrooms are cooked through and have released their excess moisture. Add the spring onions, oyster sauce and pepper to taste. Mix the cornstarch with the water, sufficient to form a thick paste with the mushroom mix. Depending on the quantity of moisture in the mushrooms, the actual quantity of cornstarch required will vary. Set aside to cool.

To make the dough, dissolve the sugar in the warm water and stir in the yeast. Allow to ferment for 10 minutes. Mix the flours together and add the fermented yeast. Mix well and knead to a smooth dough (about 10 minutes). Cover and set aside in a warm place and allow to prove for 30 minutes.

Roll the dough into a 5 cm diameter log and cut into 16 pieces. Place each piece on a lightly-floured board and roll out to about 1 cm thick.

Place a spoonful of the mushroom mix in the centre of each disk. Moisten the edges and fold up to form a bun, leaving a small opening at the top. Place each bun on a small square of lightly-oiled greaseproof paper. Arrange on a steaming basket, leaving at least 3-4 cm between each bun. Repeat until all are prepared. Set aside in a warm place for 15-20 minutes for the buns to prove and double in size.

Meanwhile, fill the steamer base with water and bring to a rapid boil. As soon as the buns are ready, place the steamer trays onto the base and steam over rapidly boiling water for 10-12 minutes. Serve.

Vegetable Moussaka

Serves: 12 Calories: 115 Fat: 1.1 gm

- 300 gm eggplants
- 200 gm potatoes
- 150 gm cracked wheat
- 5 whole tomatoes
- 50 ml vegetable stock
- 2 sprigs fresh oregano
- 1/2 tsp ground nutmeg
- 100 ml tomato juice
- 2 tsp Chiva-Som salt substitute (see page 136)
- 1 tomato, seeded and chopped
- 1/2 medium onion, chopped

Tomato sauce
- 7 tomatoes
- 60 basil leaves
- Chiva-Som salt substitute
- vegetable stock

White sauce
- 180 ml low-fat milk
- 25 gm cornstarch

Cut the eggplants lengthwise into 1 cm thick slices. Wash and set aside to drain for 5 minutes. In a heated non-stick pan, cook the eggplants on one side only until the slices start to soften. Remove to a tray and set aside. Peel and slice the potatoes, then place in boiling water and cook until just soft. Do not overcook or slices will break up. Cut the tomatoes into 1/2 cm thick slices and set aside.

In a large heavy-based pot place the vegetable stock, onion, garlic and the seeded and chopped tomato and cook until the onion is transparent. Add a little vegetable stock if it becomes too dry. Add the cracked wheat, tomato juice, half of the salt substitute, oregano and nutmeg, and simmer until the wheat has cooked through (8-10 minutes).

To make the white sauce, in a separate saucepan mix the cornstarch with the milk and slowly bring to the boil. Stirring continuously, cook through for 3-4 minutes. The mix should be thick but pourable. Cover and set aside in a warm place.

For the moussaka, in a rectangle earthenware dish place the eggplant slices. Follow in order with the potato slices, cracked wheat mix, tomato slices and white sauce. Bake in a moderate oven for 15 minutes.

To make the tomato sauce, take the tomatoes, basil and some vegetable stock and place in a blender. Pulse blend until almost smooth. Pour into a saucepan and simmer for 10-15 minutes. Add salt substitute to season to taste.

When the moussaka is cooked, remove from the oven and cut into serving portions. Place on serving plates and spoon accompanying sauce over. Serve.

Vegetable moussaka

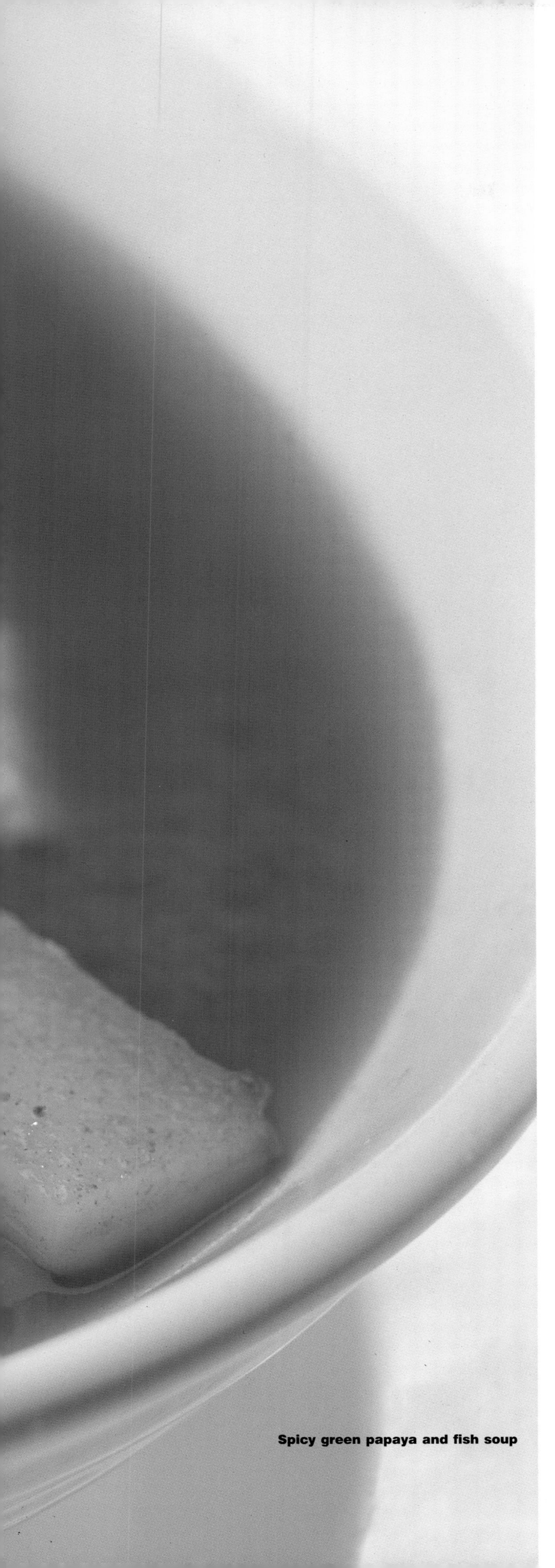

Spicy green papaya and fish soup

3 Soups

Spicy Green Papaya and Fish Soup

Serves: 2 Calories: 105 Fat: 2.3 gm

- 100 gm snapper fillet, cubed
- 500 ml water
- 1/2 tsp orange curry paste
- 1/2 tsp red curry paste (see page 147)
- 120 gm green papaya, diced
- 1/2 tsp soy sauce
- 2 dried chillies
- 1 tsp apple concentrate
- 1/2 tsp tamarind juice (or lime juice)

In a pot, place the fish and the water. Bring to the boil and simmer until well cooked. Place the fish and the liquid into a food processor with the dried chillies and the curry pastes. Blend until smooth, then put back into the pot.

Add the diced green papaya and simmer until cooked. Season to taste with soy sauce, then highlight the flavours with the apple concentrate and tamarind juice. Serve.

If a chunkier soup is required, blend only half of the fish, leaving the rest in cubes.

Spicy Black Bean Soup

Serves: 8 Calories: 130 Fat: 0.8 gm

- 2 cups dried black beans
- 2 onions, chopped
- 4 cloves garlic, crushed
- 1 tsp red or cayenne pepper powder
- 1 tbsp cumin seeds
- 1 tbsp coriander seeds
- 1/2 tsp chilli powder
- 1 1/2 tsp oregano, ground
- 1 1/2 tsp sage, ground
- 1/2 tsp Chiva-Som salt substitute (see page 144)
- black pepper
- 4 jalapeno peppers
- 2 medium tomatoes, chopped
- 10 cups vegetable stock
- 1/2 cup coriander leaves
- 1/2 cup lime juice

Soak the black beans in cold water overnight. Next day, strain the beans and set aside. In a small pot place 1/4 cup of vegetable stock with the chopped onions, garlic, cayenne, cumin, coriander seeds, oregano, sage, chilli powder and salt substitute.

Cook over a medium heat, stirring continuously until it forms a dry paste.

Add the drained beans, black pepper, jalapeno chillies, tomatoes and remaining vegetable stock. Stir and bring to the boil. Simmer until the beans are cooked, approximately 20 minutes.

Allow to cool slightly, then add the coriander and process with a blender until smooth.

Season with the lime juice (if needed you can add a little soy sauce) and serve with a little extra chopped coriander on top.

Spicy black bean soup

Gazpacho

Serves: 2 Calories: 90 Fat: 1.3 gm

- 500 gm ripe tomatoes
- 1 green bell pepper
- 1 medium brown onion
- 1 red bell pepper
- 1/2 medium cucumber
- 2 cloves garlic
- 150 ml vegetable stock (or as required)
- 12 basil leaves
- 1 tbsp soy sauce
- pepper to taste

Wash all the vegetables carefully and pat dry. Cut a small cross in the base of each tomato and plunge into boiling water for 5-10 seconds or until the skin starts to split. Using a slotted spoon, carefully remove the tomatoes and plunge into a bowl of ice-cold water. This will "shock" the skin and make it easier to peel. Peel the tomatoes, cut them in half and remove the seeds. Remove the seeds from the bell peppers and roughly chop them. Peel and roughly chop the onion.

Place the tomatoes, bell peppers, cucumber, peeled garlic cloves and half of the basil leaves in a food processor. Blend until smooth, adding as much vegetable stock as is necessary to ensure a thick soup-like consistency. Season to taste with the soy sauce and pepper and chill well before serving. To serve, garnish with the reserved basil leaves finely shredded.

If you do not have time to chill the soup, add half a cup of ice together with the vegetables and process until smooth. Done this way, you don't need to add the extra vegetable stock.

Brown onion is recommended for this dish as it is milder in taste.

Gazpacho

Rich vegetable soup

Rich Vegetable Soup

Serves: 6 Calories: 130 Fat: 1.5 gm

- 25 gm pearl barley
- 25 gm split peas
- 25 gm green or red lentils
- 2 medium onions, chopped
- 1 large parsnip, cubed
- 1 large potato, cubed
- 2 medium carrots, diced
- 1.2 litres vegetable stock
- 2 sprigs fresh rosemary
- 2 sprigs fresh thyme
- 3 tsp soy sauce
- black pepper

Wash the pearl barley, split peas and lentils under running water until it runs clear. Place in a large pot with the vegetable stock and bring to the boil. Lower the heat and cook for another 10-15 minutes.

Add the prepared vegetables, herbs and seasoning and continue to simmer until all is cooked.

Adjust the seasoning with black pepper if necessary and serve.

Spicy Vegetable Soup (Kaeng Liang)

Serves: 4 Calories: 130 Fat: 1.4 gm

- 2 cm fresh galangal
- 3 shallots
- 1 tsp brown miso paste
- 1 tsp ground black pepper
- 100 gm straw mushrooms
- 1 cup fresh baby corn, cooked
- 200 gm pumpkin
- 1 medium sponge gourd
- 2 spring onions
- 1 litre vegetable stock
- 1 tsp light soy sauce
- 1/2 cup Thai sweet basil leaves

Pound the pepper, galangal, shallots and miso paste together in a mortar to mix to a paste. Alternatively, place all in a blender. The mixture need not be smooth. Place the spice mix in a saucepan with the vegetable stock.

Cut the pumpkin and gourd into cubes. Cut the baby corn to the same size. Roughly chop the mushrooms and add to the pot with the pumpkin and corn and cook until the pumpkin is tender. Add the sponge gourd and continue to simmer until it is just done. Adjust the seasoning with the soy sauce. Remove from the heat and add basil leaves to serve.

Spicy vegetable soup (kaeng liang)

Thai chicken noodle soup

Thai Chicken Noodle Soup

Serves: 6 Calories: 120 Fat: 1.9 gm

- 2 litres vegetable stock
- 1 onion, shredded
- 6 cloves garlic, crushed
- 5 cloves
- 300 gm cabbage, shredded
- 5 tsp soy sauce
- 2 tbsp rice vinegar
- black pepper
- 200 gm thin fresh rice noodles
- 300 gm skinless chicken breast, shredded
- 1 cup beansprouts
- 1 spring onion, chopped
- 2 tbsp coriander leaves, chopped
- 1 large red chilli, sliced

In a large pot, place the vegetable stock and bring to the boil. Add the shredded onion, crushed garlic, shredded cabbage, cloves, soy sauce, vinegar and chilli.

Simmer for 15-20 minutes then strain, reserving the liquid. You should have 1.2 litres of liquid. Adjust flavour with fresh black pepper if necessary.

Add the stock back to the pot, and bring to simmer again. Add the shredded chicken breast and the noodles. Simmer until the noodles are heated through and the chicken is just cooked.

Spoon into warmed soup bowls. Pile with beansprouts and chopped spring onion and coriander. Decorate with sliced red chilli and serve.

Chiva-Som Gumbo

Serves: 6 Calories: 135 Fat: 1.1 gm

- 1 green bell pepper, chopped
- 1 onion, chopped
- 1/2 cup celery (with leaves), finely shredded
- 2 cloves garlic, crushed
- 2 cups fresh tomato puree
- 1 bay leaf
- 1 tsp Cajun or Creole seasoning
- 1 dried chilli
- 1 cup fresh corn kernels, uncooked
- 1.5 litres vegetable stock
- 1 cup fresh okra, thickly sliced
- 12 medium prawn tails, shelled and de-veined

Combine the onion, bell pepper, celery, garlic, tomato puree, vegetable stock, bay leaf, Cajun or Creole seasoning and dried chilli into a large saucepan. Slowly bring to the boil.

Once boiling, reduce the heat to low, cover and simmer for 10 minutes or until the vegetables are tender. Add the corn and okra. Bring back to the boil and simmer for 5-10 minutes.

Add the shrimp to the gumbo, and simmer until the shrimp turns pink and is cooked through. Serve.

Chiva-Som gumbo

Greek salad, Chiva-Som style

4
Salads

Greek Salad, Chiva-Som style

Serves: 4 Calories: 125 Fat: 4.6 gm

- 1/3 cup low-fat ricotta cheese
- 4 cups mixed lettuce
- 4 tomatoes, cut into wedges
- 12 black olives
- 1 green bell pepper, roasted
- 1 red bell pepper, roasted
- 4 tbsp balsamic salad dressing
- 1 head of romaine (cos) lettuce

Pulse blend the ricotta in a blender until smooth. Place on a tray covered with plastic food wrap and shape into a square approximately 1/2 cm thick. Chill in the refrigerator.

Wash the mixed lettuce carefully and pat dry. Remove the seeds from the olives. Shred the roasted bell peppers. Place all in a large bowl with the tomato wedges and toss. Place romaine lettuce in a serving plate/bowl to give the salad height and pile tossed salad on top. Pour dressing over. Carefully cut the prepared cheese into cubes and place on top of the salad. Serve.

Mackerel salad

Mackerel Salad

Serves: 1 Calories: 200 Fat: 3.9 gm

- 100 gm mackerel fillet
- 2 spring onions
- 1 tbsp fresh ginger, cubed
- 1 shallot
- 1 tsp almonds, roasted and chopped
- 1/2 small green mango
- 2 tbsp lime juice
- 1/2 lime zest
- 3 lettuce leaves
- coriander for garnish

Cut the mackerel into cubes and steam to cook. Set aside to cool. Meanwhile slice the spring onions and shallot. Dice the green mango. Mix the spring onions, shallot and mango with the ginger, almonds and lemon juice. Carefully fold through the cold mackerel fillet. Serve piled on top of the lettuce leaves and garnish with the coriander.

Tempeh Salad

Serves: 4 Calories: 130 Fat: 4.0 gm

- 160 gm tempeh
- 2 large carrots, grated
- 2 daikon white turnips, grated
- 2 beetroots, grated
- 40 ml apple cider vinegar
- 2 tsp sesame seeds
- 1 sheet nori, sliced into strips

Slice the tempeh thinly and in a non-stick pan, "fry" on both sides without any oil. Remove.

Arrange a row of each of the grated vegetables on a serving plate. Arrange the warm tempeh on top, sprinkle with sesame seeds and apple cider vinegar. Garnish with fine strips of nori.

When "frying" the tempeh, if it sticks to the pan, that means the pan is not hot enough.

Tempeh salad

Tomato and barley salad (page 90)

Tomato and Barley Salad

Serves: 4 Calories: 130 Fat: 1.6 gm

- 8 medium tomatoes
- 2 cups coriander
- 4 tbsp balsamic vinegar
- 4 tbsp barley kernels
- 1 tbsp apple concentrate
- 5 gm mustard powder
- 2 butterhead lettuce leaves (or leaves of choice)

Oven roast the barley until it has a nutty smell, remove and cool. Place into a coffee grinder or blender and process until ground, but not a powder. Cut the tomatoes into quarters and remove the seeds. Cut into strips. Set aside.

In a small bowl mix the mustard powder, apple concentrate and balsamic vinegar together. Roughly chop the coriander and place in the bowl with the sliced tomatoes. Arrange the lettuce leaves on a plate. Toss the tomato mix with the dressing and serve on the lettuce immediately to maintain the textures.

Chicken salad, Thai style

Chicken Salad, Thai style

Serves: 4 Calories: 150 Fat: 2.3 gm

- 400 gm skinless chicken breast, poached and shredded
- 3 tomatoes
- 2 sticks celery
- 1 onion
- 4 spring onions
- 1 bunch coriander
- 2 cloves garlic, crushed
- 2 bird chillies (or to taste)
- 1 tbsp plus 1 tsp lemon juice
- 1 tsp light soy sauce
- 8 lettuce leaves
- 2 tsp apple concentrate (or 1 tsp honey)

Combine the lemon juice with soy sauce, apple concentrate or honey and crushed garlic. Set aside. De-seed the tomatoes, then cut the tomatoes, celery and onion into matchsticks. Shred the spring onions, and finely chop the chillies. Roughly chop the coriander. Combine all ingredients together and serve on the lettuce leaves with extra coriander for decoration.

Miang Kham

Serves: 10 Calories: 95 Fat: 4.5 gm

- 50 miang kham leaves (wild pepper leaves) or kale or lettuce
- 100 gm shredded coconut, toasted
- 100 gm almonds, roasted and roughly chopped
- 80 gm ginger roots, diced
- 80 gm limes, diced with skin
- 20 gm chillies, chopped
- 200 gm shallots, diced

Sauce

- 1 cup honey
- 1 1/2 cups water
- 1/2 cup almonds, roasted
- 1 tsp salt
- 1/2 cup shredded coconut, toasted

Arrange all the ingredients on a plate in separate bowls. To eat, make a small cup from a miang kham leaf (or leaf of choice) and place a little of each of the ingredients in it as required. Top with the sauce.

To make the sauce, add all ingredients together in a heavy-based saucepan and bring to the boil. Reduce the heat and simmer for about 10 minutes. Skim as necessary. Remove from the heat and allow to cool. Pulse blend to a smooth sauce.

Miang kham

Salmon with garam masala

Fish

Salmon with Garam Masala

Serves: 4 Calories: 265 Fat: 15.3 gm

- 4 x 140 gm salmon steaks
- 10 gm garam masala powder (see page 143)
- 2 tomatoes
- 120 ml fresh tomato sauce
- 4-5 sprigs purple basil

Cut the tomatoes in quarters, remove the seeds and cut into slices. Set aside. Heat a heavy-based metal frying pan. Coat the salmon steaks in the garam masala powder and place in a frying pan. Cook for 15-20 seconds to seal, taking care not to burn the spices. Remove and place the pan in a moderate oven. Cook for 4-5 minutes or until done.

To serve, heat the tomato sauce and spoon on the serving plate. Place the salmon steak on top, then decorate with the tomato slices and sprigs of purple basil.

Excellent accompanied by a crisp garden salad containing plenty of fresh herbs.

Red Snapper Curry

Serves: 4 Calories: 300 Fat: 4.7 gm

- 480 gm red snapper
- 30 gm green chillies
- 2 tbsp orange curry paste
- 30 gm red chillies
- 1 tbsp turmeric powder
- 1/2 cup pea eggplants
- 1/2 cup Thai basil leaves
- 4 white eggplants
- 1 tbsp light soy sauce
- 1 kaffir lime leaf
- 2 cups vegetable stock
- 1/2 cup low-fat milk
- 2 tbsp cornstarch
- 4 tbsp water
- 2 cups steamed brown rice

Cut the fish into bite-size chunks. Roll chop the chillies and cut the white eggplants into quarters. In a heavy-based pan, gently "fry" the curry paste with turmeric powder and a little of the vegetable stock until almost dry.

Add the fish and mix thoroughly with the paste. Add the remaining stock, chillies, pea eggplants and soy sauce. Simmer for 3-5 minutes, or until the eggplants are cooked (soft).

Mix the cornstarch with the water and add to thicken the sauce until it coats the back of a spoon. Add the basil leaves and mix through.

Shred a bit of chilli and decorate with a sprig of basil. Serve with the steamed brown rice.

Blackened Pomfret with Okra

Serves: 4 Calories: 250 Fat: 2.2 gm

- 4 x 150 gm fillets of pomfret
- 1 tsp black pepper
- 1 tsp dried chilli powder
- 1 tsp white pepper
- 1/2 tsp oregano, ground
- 1/2 tsp onion powder
- 1/2 tsp thyme, ground
- 2 bell peppers, baked
- 2 sweet potatoes, baked
- 8 baby okra, baked
- 1/2 tsp Chiva-Som salt substitute (see page 144)
- 1/4 cup vegetable stock

Red snapper curry

Blackened pomfret with okra

Put all the spices in a bowl and mix well. Place the fish fillets on a plate and heavily coat with the spices on both sides. In a non-stick pan, bring the vegetable stock to the boil and simmer until almost dry.

Place the fish and cook for 1-2 minutes by adding a little more vegetable stock if it becomes too dry. Turn and cook the second side. Do not turn back to the first side. When cooked, serve with the baked bell peppers, okras and sweet potatoes.

Stir-Fried Glass Noodles with Seafood

Serves: 6 Calories: 180 Fat: 4.4 gm

- 250 gm dried glass noodles (vermicelli)
- 1/2 cup beansprouts
- 100 gm carrots, shredded
- 1/2 cup vegetable stock
- 1/2 tsp dried red chilli powder
- 3 cloves garlic, chopped
- 1 cm fresh ginger, grated
- 30 ml fish sauce (nam pla)
- 60 ml lemon juice
- 400 gm assorted fresh diced seafood (prawns, squid, seabass)
- 4 spring onions
- coriander and sweet basil leaves to taste

Soak noodles in warm water for 5 minutes. Drain and leave in a bowl handy for use. In a wok, heat and "stir-fry" the chilli powder, garlic and ginger. Add a little vegetable stock if it sticks or starts to get too hot and burn. Mix in the shredded carrots. Toss and remove.

Place the diced seafood in the wok and cook to colour. Add the carrot mix back to the wok, and put in the spring onions, nam pla, beansprouts and lemon juice. Toss together.

Put in the noodles and heat through, adding a little extra stock if the mix becomes too dry.

Chop the coriander and add with basil leaves to taste. Toss together and serve.

Stir-fried glass noodles with seafood

Tuna Steak with Tomato and Salad

Serves: 4 Calories: 190 Fat: 3.5 gm

- 4 x 110 gm tuna steaks
- 4 tomatoes
- Chiva-Som salt substitute (see page 144)
- 4 spring onions
- 4 cups salad leaves
- 2 tbsp apple concentrate
- 50 ml cider vinegar
- 3 shallots, finely chopped
- 1 tbsp soy sauce
- 1/2 cup coriander leaves

Season the tuna steaks heavily with the salt substitute on both sides. Cut the tomatoes in half and discard the seeds. Dice the flesh and put into a small bowl. Chop the spring onions finely and add to the tomatoes with the vinegar, apple concentrate, soy sauce and finely chopped shallots. Set aside.

In a very hot non-stick pan sear the tuna steaks, adding a little vegetable stock if the tuna looks too dry. Arrange the salad leaves on a serving plate, top with the seared tuna and spoon the sauce over. Decorate liberally with coriander leaves. Serve.

Steamed Fish and Cabbage Custard (Hor Mok)

Serves: 8 Calories: 125 Fat: 1.0 gm

- 600 gm fresh snapper fillets
- 2 cups skim milk
- 1 tbsp red curry paste (see page 147)
- 1 tbsp raw sugar
- 3 egg whites, beaten
- 3 tsp fish sauce (nam pla)
- 24 Thai basil leaves
- 2 cups finely shredded Chinese cabbage
- 3 kaffir lime leaves, shredded
- 2 fresh red chillies, shredded

Cut the fish into small cubes and place in a bowl with the curry paste. Alternatively, place the fish and curry paste in a food processor, and pulse blend until well mixed. Add the milk and mix again. Add the fish sauce, sugar and lightly beaten egg whites. Mix thoroughly.

Blanch the chopped cabbage in boiling water for 1 minute. Refresh under cold running water. Drain and squeeze dry. Divide amongst the cup moulds, followed by the basil leaves. Then fill the cups with the curried fish mix, and finish with the shredded lime leaves and shredded chillies. Place in a steamer and cook for 12-15 minutes, or until set. Garnish with additional finely shredded basil leaves and chillies.

Tuna steak with tomato and salad

Steamed fish and cabbage custard (hor mok)

Spicy Steamed Seabass

Serves: 2 Calories: 240 Fat: 1.4 gm

- 300 gm seabass fillets
- black pepper
- 3 spring onions
- 2 red chillies
- 1 clove garlic
- 1 cm fresh ginger
- 60 ml Chinese wine
- 60 ml soy sauce
- 15 gm coriander leaves

Carefully remove any bones from the seabass. Season the fish with pepper and leave for 2-3 minutes. Slice the spring onions and shred the chillies and ginger. Chop the garlic. Mix all the vegetables with soy sauce and wine. Spoon over the fish and place in a steamer over heat until cooked through. Remove from the steamer and place on a serving plate. Sprinkle with coriander leaves (and extra chillies if desired). Serve.

Chermoula Seabass with Bok Choy

Serves: 4 Calories: 230 Fat: 3.0 gm

- 480 gm red snapper fillet
- 2 tbsp parsley
- 6 tbsp coriander
- 40 gm shallots
- 1$^1/_2$ tsp cumin, ground
- 1$^1/_2$ tsp paprika
- $^1/_4$ tsp chilli powder
- 2 tbsp lemon juice
- $^1/_2$ tsp white pepper
- 1 tbsp soy sauce
- 60 ml vegetable stock
- 4 cups of bok choy

Spicy steamed seabass

Chermoula seabass with bok choy

Place the parsley, half the coriander, shallots, paprika, cumin, chilli powder, lemon juice and soy sauce in a blender and process until smooth. Pour into a small dish just large enough to hold the fish fillets.

Add the fillets of snapper without the skin, or firm-fleshed fish of your choice, and turn to coat well. Leave to marinade in the refrigerator for at least 2 hours.

To cook, take the fillets from the marinade, reserving the liquid to make the sauce. Place in a hot non-stick pan, adding a little vegetable stock to prevent the fish from burning. This will also help to release the fish from the pan, making it easier to turn. Let the stock evaporate, then turn the fish over with a non-metal spatula to avoid scratching the non-stick pan.

Meanwhile cook the bok choy in boiling water. Do not over-cook. Drain and arrange on a serving plate. Top with the cooked fish, then working quickly add the remaining marinade to the pan with sufficient water to make a sauce. Bring to the boil quickly and spoon around the fish. Decorate with the remaining coriander and serve immediately.

Sweet and Sour Kingfish

Serves: 2 Calories: 180 Fat: 0.9 gm

- 1/4 cup vegetable stock
- 220 gm kingfish
- 1/2 cup pineapple, diced
- 1/2 cup sweetcorn
- 1 cucumber, seeded and diced
- 1 onion, diced
- 2 tomatoes, seeded and diced
- 3 spring onions
- 1 small chilli
- 2 tbsp soy sauce
- 2 tsp cornstarch

Place the vegetable stock and diced onion in a saucepan and bring to the boil. Add the sweetcorn, cucumber, pineapple and tomatoes. Cover and simmer until soft, but not overcooked.

In a separate pot of boiling water, blanch the kingfish. Add the chopped spring onions and chilli. Season to taste with the soy sauce. Add a little more vegetable stock if it is too dry. Simmer for a further 1-2 minutes. Thicken with cornstarch, cook for a further 2 minutes and serve.

If the pineapple is a good, ripe one, no sweetener is required. If it is not full-flavoured, you may need to add up to 1 tsp of apple concentrate (20 calories/tsp).

Sweet and sour kingfish

Poached Halibut with Coriander

Serves: 4 Calories: 240 Fat: 4.1 gm

- 4 x 120 gm halibut steaks
- 5 gm cinnamon stick
- 1/2 tsp turmeric powder
- 1 tsp anise seeds
- 1 1/2 cups vegetable stock
- 2 tbsp soy sauce
- 750 gm kale or spinach
- 1 tsp cornstarch
- 1 cup coriander leaves

In a saucepan just large enough to hold the steaks, place the vegetable stock and the spices. Bring to the boil and simmer for 2-3 minutes.

Strain the liquid. Return this to the saucepan and add the soy sauce and the halibut steaks (or your choice of similar firm-fleshed fish). Simmer for 3-4 minutes or until just cooked. Remove the fish and keep warm.

Thicken half of the cooking liquid with the cornstarch for the sauce.

Meanwhile prepare and steam the kale (or spinach). Place the kale in the centre of the serving plate and top with the cooked halibut steaks and pour over the sauce. Sprinkle with coriander leaves and serve.

Poached halibut with coriander

Pan-fried breast of turkey with onion and olive pizza

6 Meat

Pan-fried Breast of Turkey with Onion and Olive Pizza

Serves: 4 Calories: 290 Fat: 9.5 gm

- 4 x 110 gm turkey breast steaks
- 1/4 cup vegetable stock
- 4 pcs wholewheat pizza dough
- 2 onions, shredded
- 12 black olives, sliced
- 1 cup chicken stock
- 4 sprigs fresh chervil or tarragon
- 4 cups broccoli florets

Wholewheat pizza dough

- 7 gm dried yeast
- 2 tsp apple concentrate
- 250 ml warm water
- 2 cups flour
- 2 cups wholemeal flour
- 1 tbsp butter
- pinch of salt

To make the pizza dough, combine the yeast, apple concentrate and warm water and leave in a warm place to prove. Meanwhile mix the flours, salt and butter to a fine crumb. Add the yeast mix and knead for 4-5 minutes. Set aside to prove until double in size. Knock back the dough and shape as required. Top the pizza dough with the shredded onions and two-thirds of the sliced olives. Bake in a hot oven for 6-10 minutes.

Add the vegetable stock to a heavy-based pan and "pan-fry" the turkey breast. Meanwhile, place the chicken stock in a small saucepan and reduce over high heat by three-quarters. To serve, steam the broccoli and place on the side of the plate. Arrange the pizza in the middle, slice the turkey and arrange on top. Spoon the reduced chicken stock around. Decorate with the remaining olive slices.

Beef with Garlic and Pepper, Thai style

Serves: 4 Calories: 250 Fat: 6.0 gm

- 400 gm beef tenderloin
- 2 cloves garlic, crushed
- 20 gm green peppercorns
- 2 tbsp oyster sauce
- 1 tbsp soy sauce
- 200 ml vegetable stock
- 2 tsp dark soy sauce
- 1 tsp cornstarch
- 2 tbsp cold water

Trim the beef, then cut into thin slices. In a heavy-based pan, heat the crushed garlic with 30 ml vegetable stock. Add the beef and toss to cook until dry. Add another 30 ml vegetable stock and cook until dry again. Add the remaining vegetable stock, green peppercorns, oyster and soy sauce and bring to the boil. Mix the cornstarch with the cold water. Add sufficient to the beef mix to thicken the sauce slightly. Serve with steamed brown rice.

Veal Tenderloin topped with Spinach Mousse

Serves: 5 Calories: 280 Fat: 8.2 gm

- 550 gm veal tenderloin fillet
- 100 gm spinach, blanched
- 3 sheets wholewheat filo pastry
- 1 tsp soy sauce
- 1 tsp Chiva-Som salt substitute (see page 144)
- 1 tbsp yoghurt

Trim the veal and divide into 50 gm portions. Make sure the trimmings are free of fat and sinew and place this and the spinach into a blender and blend until fine. Do not let the mix get hot. Add the salt substitute and soy sauce for the mousse.

Take the veal portions and set them all top to bottom (i.e. with the grain of the meat running up and down). Cut the filo pastry to the same height as the veal, and wrap around each portion, using the yoghurt to make it stick. Top with the mousse, about 25 gm for each portion, then bake in a hot oven for 5-7 minutes. Let rest for another 2-3 minutes before serving so the juices can settle.

Beef with garlic and pepper, Thai style

Veal tenderloin topped with spinach mousse

Stir-fried veal, Chinese style (page 106)

Stir-fried Veal, Chinese style

Serves: 4 Calories: 280 Fat: 4.7 gm

- 100 gm onions, sliced
- 440 gm veal loin
- 30 gm ginger root, shredded
- 2 cloves garlic, minced
- 50 gm dried shiitake mushrooms, soaked and sliced
- 2 tbsp Chinese wine
- 10 gm spring onions, sliced
- 10 gm cornstarch
- 1.5 tbsp soy sauce
- 30 gm red chillies
- 2 cups steamed brown rice
- 175 ml vegetable stock

Trim and slice the veal into thin slices, then put back into the refrigerator. Arrange in separate bowls the ginger, garlic, shiitake mushrooms, spring onions and onions. Roll chop the red chillies with most of the seeds removed (or leave all of the seeds for added spiciness). In a bowl mix the wine, soy sauce and cornstarch.

Heat a wok or large skillet and when hot, add the onions, garlic and ginger and toss them. Add about 30 ml of the vegetable stock.

Continue to stir and add the ingredients in the following order: shiitake mushrooms, veal, remaining vegetable stock and chillies.

Once the stock starts to evaporate a little and the colour begins to brown, add the cornstarch mix, stirring the contents of the wok to avoid lumps. This will thicken the liquid so that it coats the back of a spoon. Remove into a serving dish and serve with the steamed brown rice.

Lamb cutlets with garden vegetables and rosemary jus

Minted lamb with couscous

Lamb Cutlets with Garden Vegetables and Rosemary Jus

Serves: 1 Calories: 310 Fat: 8.0 gm

- 110 gm lamb cutlets
- black pepper
- 2 sprigs fresh rosemary
- 2 tbsp meat glaze
- 2 tbsp mashed sweet potato
- 100 ml vegetable stock
- 1 cup fresh vegetables of choice (carrots, asparagus, peas, etc)

Trim the lamb of all sinew and fat, and season the lamb with pepper and fresh rosemary. Leave for 20-30 minutes. In a non-stick pan, "fry" the lamb with a little vegetable stock until done. Add a little extra vegetable stock if the lamb starts to stick. Alternatively, place the lamb on a grill. When done, remove the lamb to a warm plate and set aside.

For the sauce, add the meat glaze to the pan and the remaining vegetable stock. Boil rapidly to reduce to about 2 tbsp. Meanwhile, steam the vegetables and reheat the mashed potato. Place the vegetables on a serving plate and the lamb cutlets on top. Arrange the mashed potato on the side, and pour the sauce over.

Minted Lamb with Couscous

Serves: 4 Calories: 330 Fat: 6.9 gm

- 440 gm lean lamb loin
- 50 gm mint leaves
- 100 ml vegetable stock
- 1 tbsp soy sauce
- 1 medium carrot, finely cubed
- 1 cup green peas
- 2 cups couscous, cooked
- 80 ml low-fat yoghurt
- 1 tsp tamari soy sauce
- 1 clove garlic, chopped
- 1/4 tsp black pepper
- 80 ml brown gravy

Place the mint leaves, soy sauce and vegetable stock in a blender, and blend to a paste. Place the lamb into a deep dish, pour over the mint paste and leave to marinate overnight so that the mint infuses into the meat. Mix the yoghurt, garlic, pepper and tamari soy sauce together in a small bowl, then cover and refrigerate overnight.

Blanch the carrot and peas and set aside. In a pot, cook the couscous then add the blanched vegetables, season to taste, cover and keep warm. Using a heavy-based pan, cook the lamb loin by putting it into the hot pan, turn it over after 1 minute, then place the pan into a hot oven for 5 minutes (make sure that the pan has no plastic handle). Remove from the oven and place on a plate and cover to keep warm for a couple of minutes while finishing the sauce. (This also helps to let the blood settle in the meat so there is little excess when cutting.)

To make the sauce, add a little water to the pan to deglaze it. Then add the brown gravy and stir gently until it comes to a boil. To serve, cut the lamb into thick slices at a 45 degree angle, then place the couscous in the centre of the serving plates to make a bed for the lamb. Place the lamb on the couscous and pour the gravy over it. Finally, drizzle the prepared garlic yoghurt over the top and serve.

Chicken with Nori and Herbs
Serves: 4 Calories: 230 Fat: 2.5 gm

- 5 x 100 gm skinless chicken breast
- 2 sheets nori
- 1 ice cube
- 1/2 cup vegetable stock
- 1 tbsp soy sauce
- 1 large carrot
- 8 pieces baby corn
- 2 courgettes
- 60 gm snow peas
- 1 tbsp Chiva-Som salt substitute (see page 144)
- 2 tbsp parsley, chopped

Place 100 gm of the chicken breast in a food processor with the nori, half of the soy sauce and the ice cube. Pulse blend until almost smooth. Cut a pocket into each of the remaining chicken breasts and fill with the nori mix. Sprinkle with the salt substitute and refrigerate until needed.

Peel and cut the vegetables into even sizes and cook in a steamer. Heat a heavy-based pan and add a little of the vegetable stock. When hot, add the chicken breasts. Continue to cook on a medium heat for 5-8 minutes, adding a little extra vegetable stock if it becomes too dry. Do not overcook the chicken.

To serve, arrange the vegetables and chicken on a serving plate and spoon over a few drops of the cooking juice from the pan.

Chicken with nori and herbs

Ethiopian Chicken Stew
Serves: 5 Calories: 300 Fat: 3.8 gm

- 500 gm skinless chicken breast
- 2 onions, chopped
- 6 cloves garlic
- 2 tsp cayenne pepper
- 1 tsp cumin, ground
- 1 tsp cardamom, ground
- 1 tsp nutmeg, ground
- 1 tsp fennel seeds, ground
- 400 ml vegetable stock
- 1/4 cup tomato paste
- 1 tbsp soy sauce
- 1 tsp black pepper
- 1/2 cup coriander leaves
- 1/2 cup berbere
- 1 large carrot
- 10 pieces baby corn
- 2 cups steamed brown rice
- 4 new potatoes

Berbere (makes about 2 cups)
- 1/2 tsp cumin, ground
- 2 tbsp chilli flakes
- 1/2 tsp cardamom, ground
- 1/2 tsp black pepper
- 1/4 tsp all spice, ground
- 1/2 tsp cloves, ground
- 1/4 tsp coriander seeds, ground
- 2 tbsp paprika
- 1/4 tsp fenugreek seeds
- 1/2 tsp sea salt
- 1/4 tsp cinnamon, ground
- 1/2 cup cayenne pepper powder
- 4 cloves garlic, crushed
- 300 ml vegetable stock (or as required)

Ethiopian chicken stew

Cut the chicken into cubes. Peel and prepare the vegetables, cutting them to the same size as the chicken. In a large heavy-based saucepan, cook the onions and garlic in a little vegetable stock until the vegetable stock has evaporated. Add the spices and continue to cook until fragrant, adding extra vegetable stock if it becomes too dry. Add the tomato paste, soy sauce, pepper, berbere, chicken, prepared vegetables and vegetable stock to cover. Cover and simmer until the vegetables are tender. Serve with steamed brown rice and lots of coriander leaves.

To make the berbere, in a large heavy-based pan, place the garlic and 1/4 cup vegetable stock. Cook, stirring continuously. Add all the remaining ingredients and sufficient vegetable stock to make a paste and "fry" the spices for 3-4 minutes or until fragrant. Add extra vegetable stock if the mix becomes too dry. Store the paste in the refrigerator in an airtight, glass container until required.

Caution: This dish is spicy!

Chicken with black mushrooms

Chicken with Black Mushrooms

Serves: 4 Calories: 230 Fat: 4.0 gm

- 4 x 100 gm skinless chicken breast fillets
- 2 tbsp rice flour
- 4 shallots
- 4 dried shiitake mushrooms
- 2 cloves garlic
- 2 slices fresh ginger
- 1 tsp coriander root
- 1/2 tsp black peppercorns
- 30 ml soy sauce
- 50 ml apple concentrate
- 1/2 cup coriander leaves
- 250 ml vegetable stock

Soak the mushrooms in hot water for 5 minutes, then drain and cut into even pieces. Roll the chicken in the flour. Grind the shallots, garlic, ginger, coriander and black pepper to a paste. Add the apple concentrate and soy sauce.

In a heavy-based pan, heat 3 tbsp of vegetable stock. Add the spice paste and cook until almost dry. Add the chicken and toss to coat. Add the remaining vegetable stock and the soaked mushrooms. Cover and simmer for 10-12 minutes or until the chicken is cooked. Serve garnished liberally with coriander leaves.

Vegetable tartlet

7 Vegetables

Vegetable Tartlet

Serves: 4 Calories: 185 Fat: 4.1 gm

- 8 pcs baby corn
- 80 gm eggplants, sliced
- 1 zucchini, sliced
- 8 pcs okra
- 3 spring onions
- 12 medium asparagus spears
- 2 small red bell peppers
- 80 gm yoghurt cheese (or low-fat cottage cheese)

Pastry case

- 150 gm unsalted butter
- 200 gm plain flour
- 30 gm wholewheat flour
- 30 gm egg white
- water as needed

Sauce

- 250 ml balsamic vinegar
- 50 gm brown or raw sugar

Finely chop the spring onions and mix with the cheese. Cut all the vegetables into appropriate sizes so they can be stacked onto each other after they have been grilled. Heat the grill, barbecue or griddle pan and cook the vegetables so that they become soft, golden in colour and full of flavour. Keep them warm in a moderate oven. Place the tartlets on four individual plates, spoon the cheese on each one and stack the vegetables decoratively on top. To finish, drizzle 1 tsp of the sauce over each tartlet and some herbs, if required (basil would be a good choice).

To make the pastry case, with your fingertips crumb the cold butter and flour together. When well combined, add the egg and water. Let the pastry rest in the fridge for about 1 hour, then roll out to about 1/2 cm thickness and line 4 x 9 cm flan tins. Let rest for another hour then bake at 175C until golden brown.

To make the sauce, place the balsamic and sugar into a heavy-based pot and boil until it has reduced in volume by two-thirds. Remove from the stove and allow to cool.

Pad Thai, Chiva-Som style

Japanese tofu custard

Marinated tofu and vegetable kebabs

Ginger tofu hotpot

Pad Thai, Chiva-Som style

Serves: 4 Calories: 300 Fat: 4.9 gm

- 250 gm dried flat rice noodles
- 5 ml oil
- 1 tsp dried shrimp (or 2 tbsp fresh, chopped)
- 1 pc firm tofu, cubed
- 2 egg whites
- 1 clove garlic, crushed
- 30 ml rice vinegar
- 30 ml light soy sauce
- 1/2 tsp honey
- 2 tbsp almonds, chopped
- 4 spring onions
- 2 cups beansprouts
- fresh red chillies, shredded (optional)

Soak the dried noodles for 2 minutes in warm water to soften. Drain. In a wok or large, heavy-based, non-stick pan, heat the oil until it smokes. Add garlic and "stir-fry" for 15 seconds. Lightly beat the egg whites and mix in the tofu. Add to the pan and cook quickly.

Add the noodles, vinegar, honey and soy sauce. Toss well. Add three of the chopped spring onions, beansprouts and almonds. Cook for 2-3 minutes, stirring carefully. Serve garnished with the remaining spring onions and chillies if desired.

Marinated Tofu and Vegetable Kebabs

Makes: 10 skewers Calories: 50 per skewer Fat: 0.6 gm

- 2 small zucchinis
- 1 red bell pepper
- 1 green bell pepper
- 2 long eggplants
- 1/4 cauliflower
- 1 medium onion
- 2 pcs firm tofu, cut in squares

Marinade

- 40 ml soy sauce
- 1 tsp wasabi powder
- 1 tbsp lime juice
- 1 tsp chilli powder

Cut the vegetables into bite-size cubes. Combine the marinade ingredients together and mix well with the vegetables and tofu. Leave for 15-20 minutes. On wooden skewers that have been soaked in water, skewer alternate pieces of each vegetable and the tofu in a decorative manner. Bake in the oven, over a barbecue or under a grill for 3-4 minutes, turning to ensure that they are evenly cooked through. Serve.

Japanese Tofu Custard

Serves: 4 Calories: 75 Fat: 3.2 gm

- 225 gm firm tofu
- 2 eggs
- 4 fresh shiitake mushrooms
- 12 almonds
- 1 cup young spinach leaves, cooked
- 1 tsp mirin
- 1 tbsp light soy sauce
- 750 ml vegetable stock
- 1 sheet nori, shredded
- wasabi

Reduce the vegetable stock by half over a high heat. Set aside to cool. Dry the tofu well. Place in a blender with the almonds and puree until smooth. Add the eggs, vegetable stock, soy sauce, mirin and mix well. Thickly slice the shiitake mushrooms. Divide the cooked spinach amongst four serving cups and top each one with half of the mushrooms. Pour over the custard mix and decorate with the remaining mushrooms.

Cover each cup with baking paper and secure with a piece of string. Place in a steamer. Cover with a cloth before placing the lid of the steamer on to prevent water droplets spoiling the custard and to ensure a smooth finish. Test with a skewer after 5 minutes, and if it comes out clean the custard is cooked. If not, continue to steam until done. Serve topped with shredded nori and a little wasabi on the side for an added touch of Japan.

Ginger Tofu Hotpot

Serves: 4 Calories: 275 Fat: 3.2 gm

- 100 gm raw buckwheat kernels
- 200 gm firm tofu
- 30 ml soy sauce
- 50 gm ginger, shredded
- 2 cloves garlic, crushed
- 200 ml vegetable stock
- 200 gm cooked spinach
- some chillies (optional)
- 5 gm Chiva-Som salt substitute (see page 144)

Cut the tofu into 2 x 2 cm squares. Place the garlic, ginger, soy sauce and buckwheat kernels into a saucepan with the vegetable stock and bring to the boil. Simmer these together until two-thirds of the liquid has evaporated.

Now add the tofu, spinach and salt substitute, and cook for a further 10 minutes on a low heat. Serve in a bowl with some chillies on the side if desired.

Hot and sour garlic braised eggplant

Hot and Sour Garlic Braised Eggplant

Serves: 4 Calories: 270 Fat: 2.2 gm

- 3 long green eggplants (or 2 large purple)
- 2 medium potatoes
- 4 tomatoes
- 1 medium brown onion
- 2 cloves garlic
- 3 large red chillies, sliced
- 1 cm fresh turmeric
- 1 tbsp apple cider vinegar
- 120 ml vegetable stock
- soy sauce to taste
- 1 tsp Chiva-Som salt substitute (see page 144)

Peel and wash the potatoes. Cut the pointed ends off so that they are the same length, then slice lengthwise approximately 1 cm thick. Keep in water until needed. Slice the eggplants in half lengthwise and cut into pieces the same length as the potatoes. Slice the tomatoes into rings and leave on a plate until needed.

Slice the onion, crush the garlic and grate the turmeric. Place in a heavy-based pot and stir over a high flame. When the mix starts to stick, add a little vegetable stock. Now add the salt substitute, tomatoes, potatoes, sliced chillies, vinegar and the remainder of the stock. Stir gently then turn the flame down so that the liquid simmers, then cover and leave for 15 minutes, stirring occasionally. Add the eggplants to the pot and continue to cook for a further 5 minutes. The eggplants should be cooked but still hold its shape.

Spoon on a plate, making sure the eggplants are on top. Finish with a drizzle of soy sauce over to enhance the flavours. Serve with brown rice.

Spicy Potato Lasagne

Serves: 8 Calories: 145 Fat: 2.1 gm

- 400 gm firm tofu
- 3 cloves garlic
- 1 tsp turmeric, ground
- 1/2 medium onion
- 200 gm potatoes
- 70 gm okra
- 1 tsp Chiva-Som salt substitute (see page 144)
- 3 eggs
- 1/4 tsp paprika
- 30 ml vegetable stock
- 1/2 tsp cumin, ground
- 1/2 tsp garam masala powder (see page 143)

Spicy potato lasagne

- 1/4 tsp chilli powder
- 1/2 tsp coriander seeds, ground
- 1 tbsp soy sauce

In a blender, puree the tofu, eggs, soy sauce, onion, garlic and the powdered spices. Cut the potatoes into 1 cm thick slices and blanch them for 5 minutes in boiling water. Meanwhile cut the ends off the okra, slice into rings, and leave to the side until needed.

In a non-stick baking dish layer the tofu mix, then the potato, then the okra. Repeat the process twice more. Bake in a moderate oven for 30 minutes, uncovered. Check with a wooden skewer to see if cooked. If further cooking is required, return the dish to the oven covered in foil. To serve, turn out and cut into thick slices.

Best when served with a fresh tomato sauce.

Burmese tofu curry

Stir-fried rice noodles, Thai style

Burmese Tofu Curry

Serves: 4 Calories: 250 Fat: 2.1 gm

- 600 gm firm tofu
- 3 onions
- 1/2 tsp dried chilli powder
- 4 cloves garlic
- 1 tsp turmeric, ground
- 2 tsp ginger
- 100 ml vegetable stock
- 1/2 cup coriander, chopped
- 3 spring onions, chopped
- 2 cups steamed brown rice

In a blender, puree the onions, garlic, ginger, turmeric and chilli powder. Bring 2 tbsp of the stock to the boil and add the puree. Cook for 10-15 minutes or until rich and fragrant and all of the liquid has evaporated. (In the early stages of cooking, if the mixture appears dry yet is still not cooked, add a little more the vegetable stock.) Add the tofu and mix well. Simmer for 3-4 minutes or until the tofu takes on the turmeric colour.

Add the coriander, then remove from the heat. Fold in the spring onions and serve with the steamed brown rice.

Stir-fried Rice Noodles, Thai style

Serves: 6 Calories: 260 Fat: 2.6 gm

- 500 gm rice noodles, cooked
- 250 ml vegetable stock (or as required)
- 1/2 medium onion, shredded
- 6 cloves garlic, crushed
- 1 cup snow peas
- 6 large fresh chillies (or to taste), seeds removed and shredded
- 1 large carrot, cut into batons
- 1 cup baby corn, cut in half lengthwise
- 1 cup kale, roughly chopped
- 1 cup Thai basil leaves
- 4 tsp soy sauce

Blanch the vegetables in boiling water. Plunge into cold water to chill, drain well and set aside. In a wok or large, non-stick frying pan, place a little of the vegetable stock with the onion and garlic. Cook until transparent and almost dry, adding a little extra stock if the mix becomes too dry. Carefully pull the rice noodles apart and add to the wok or pan. Toss well, adding a little extra vegetable stock as necessary. Add the cooked vegetables and chillies to taste. Toss well to heat through. Season with soy sauce and lastly add the basil leaves. Mix well and serve.

Northern-style noodle curry soup

Northern-style Noodle Curry

Serves: 4 Calories: 225 Fat: 3.1 gm

- 200 gm egg noodles
- 1 tsp curry powder
- 2 cups young coconut water (or vegetable stock)
- 1 tbsp red curry paste (see page 147)
- 1 cup vegetable stock
- 1 tsp light soy sauce
- 2 cups mixed Asian vegetables (blanched)
- 1 litre water for boiling

Condiments

- 4 shallots, shredded
- fresh lime wedges
- 4 tsp pickled cabbage, finely sliced
- 4 tsp roasted chilli paste
- 4 tsp dark soy sauce

In a pot, place 2-3 tbsp of the vegetable stock together with the curry paste and curry powder. Stirring continuously, "fry" the paste, adding a little extra stock if it becomes too dry. Add the remaining vegetable stock, coconut water and soy sauce and reduce by a quarter. Add the vegetables.

Meanwhile in a separate pot bring the water to the boil and cook the noodles. When done, strain them, rinsing quickly under cold water to make them easier to handle but not enough to chill them. Place in individual serving bowls and pour the prepared curry mixture over the noodles. Arrange the condiments into separate small dishes for each person to season to their own taste.

Potatoes in Massaman Curry

Serves: 4 Calories: 350 Fat: 2.1 gm

- 500 gm small new potatoes, with skin
- 2 tsp massaman curry paste
- 1 cup vegetable stock (or as required)
- 2 tsp soy sauce
- 3 tsp almonds, roasted and chopped
- 1/2 cup shallots, finely diced
- 2 cups steamed brown rice

Wash the potatoes well to ensure that all the dirt is removed. Place in a saucepan with sufficient cold water to cover. Bring to the boil and simmer until cooked and drain the liquid.

Meanwhile in a heavy-based pan add a little of the vegetable stock together with the curry paste and "fry" until fragrant. Add the chopped shallots and almonds and a little more stock, and cook until the shallots are softened.

Add the cooked potatoes to the curry sauce and carefully mix, adding more vegetable stock sufficient to make a sauce. Season to taste with soy sauce. Simmer for a further 10-15 minutes to allow the flavours to infuse. Serve with steamed brown rice.

Potatoes in massaman curry

Mixed Bean Hotpot with Asian Spices

Serves: 4 Calories: 180 Fat: 8.8 gm

- 2 cups chick peas, cooked
- 1 cup red kidney beans, cooked
- 500 ml vegetable stock (or as required)
- 2 onions, shredded
- 4 cloves garlic, chopped
- 3 spring onions
- 2 cm lemongrass, finely shredded
- 1 chilli
- 1 tbsp Chiva-Som salt substitute (see page 144)
- 6 tomatoes, chopped
- 1 lemon leaf, finely shredded
- 12 Thai basil leaves, finely shredded

Place 2 tbsp of vegetable stock in a saucepan and add the onions and garlic. "Fry" over a medium heat until softened, adding a little extra stock if it becomes too dry. Add the lemongrass and tomatoes and simmer until cooked, adding more stock if the mix becomes too dry. Add the chilli and season to taste with salt substitute. Add the cooked beans and sufficient vegetable stock to just cover.

Bring to the boil and cook for 5-10 minutes or until the beans are heated through, but remain whole. Spoon into serving dishes and garnish with the finely shredded lime leaf and basil leaves.

Makes a complete meal when served with a small side salad of lettuce, diced tomato, diced cucumber and Chiva-Som garlic vinaigrette with extra coriander.

Mixed bean hotpot with Asian spices

Berry sable

Desserts

Berry Sable

Serves: 6 Calories: 110 Fat: 6.1 gm

- 1 tsp agar or 2 tsp gelatine
- 1/2 cup apple concentrate (more depending on tartness of berries)
- 12 sable biscuits (recipe following)
- 250 ml water
- 1 cup strawberries
- 1/2 cup raspberries
- 1/2 cup blueberries

Place the berries in a saucepan and add the apple concentrate. Cover and bring to the boil. Switch off immediately, so as not to overcook the fruits.

Dissolve the agar or gelatine with a little cold water. Bring the remaining water to the boil and add, stirring gently to ensure it is completely dissolved. Add the berries and mix gently, so as not to break up the fruit. Pour into a 750 ml terrine mould and chill to set (approx 2 hours). Slice to serve.

To serve, place one sable biscuit in the centre of the plate and a slice of terrine on top. Place a second biscuit at an angle, and decorate with additional fresh berries, if required. Spoon the berry coulis around. Serve.

To make the berry coulis, follow the raspberry sauce recipe instructions for the Apple Snow recipe (see page 122), but substitute raspberries with berries of choice.

Other berries of choice can be used for this recipe. If whole fresh berries are preferred, do not boil them with the apple concentrate. In the event you over-sweeten the mix, add a little lemon juice to counterbalance the taste.

Sable Biscuits

Serves: 2 Calories: 40 Fat: 5.8 gm

- 1 cup wholegrain flour
- 1/2 cup caster sugar
- 1/2 cup toasted coconut
- 1 1/2 cup rolled oats
- 1/2 cup butter
- 2 tbsp boiling water
- 1 tsp baking soda
- 1 tbsp honey

Cream the butter and sugar in a mixer, add the boiling water and honey, then slow the mixer to half-speed and add the dry ingredients. With a teaspoon drop pieces onto a non-stick mat and then flatten slightly. Bake at 165C until golden brown.

Apple Snow with Raspberry Sauce

Serves: 4 Calories: 130 Fat: 1.0 gm

- 2 cups dried apples, chopped
- 4 egg whites
- 1/4 cup apple concentrate
- 2 cups water

Sauce

- 100 ml raspberry puree
- 40 ml apple concentrate

In a saucepan, place the chopped dried apples, apple concentrate and water. Cover and simmer until softened. Leave the lid on and set aside to cool. When cold, place in a food processor and puree until smooth. Beat the egg whites to a stiff consistency and gently fold through the apple puree. Spoon into serving dishes and serve with raspberry sauce.

To make the raspberry sauce, place the raspberry puree in a small saucepan with the apple concentrate and bring to the boil. Cook for 1-2 minutes, strain and cool.

Lemon & Kiwi Sorbets

Makes: 12 x 1/2 cup portions Calories: approx 80
Fat: 0.1 gm

- 500 ml fresh fruit puree (fruit of choice)
- 2/3 cup apple concentrate (or as required)
- 1 tbsp lime juice (or as required)

Gently heat the fruit puree, adding sufficient apple concentrate and lemon juice to enhance the flavour. Do not heat too much or for too long, or the colour will be lost. Cool. Pour into an ice-cream machine and churn until frozen. Store in the freezer until required.

All fruits have different levels of sweetness or tartness depending on the type and ripeness, and this must be taken into consideration when making any frozen dessert with fruit. The fruit will also lose its sweetness once frozen.

Apple snow with raspberry sauce

Assorted home-made sorbets

Iced orange souffle

Iced Orange Souffle

Serves: 14 Calories: 135 Fat: 0.9 gm

- 500 ml orange juice
- 1 litre low-fat milk
- 4 tbsp skim milk powder
- 1 cup sugar
- 2 egg whites

Sauce

- 280 ml orange juice
- 1 tsp cornstarch
- 1 tbsp honey
- zest of 1 orange

Place the orange juice in a non-reactive pot and simmer over a high heat until it has reduced in volume by three-quarters. Cool. Reserving 2 tbsp of sugar, place the rest of the sugar, milk and milk powder in a heavy-based saucepan and cook over a low heat, stirring continuously until the sugar is dissolved. Remove from the stove and leave to cool.

Churn the cooled milk mixture in an ice-cream machine. Beat the egg whites to a firm peak then add the reserved sugar and continue beating for 1 minute. Add the reduced orange juice to the ice-cream machine and continue to churn until creamy, then add the egg white mix and continue to churn until combined. Remove the semi-frozen mix and spoon into individual moulds. Set in a freezer overnight. To serve, turn out from the mould onto a chilled plate. Spoon prepared sauce around.

To make the sauce, simmer the remaining orange juice, honey and orange zest together for 1-2 minutes. Dissolve the cornstarch in a little cold water, then use this to thicken the sauce until it coats the back of the spoon. Remove from the stove and chill.

Iced Christmas Pudding

Serves: 10 Calories: 100 Fat: 4.3 gm

- 1 litre soy ice-cream
- 1/2 cup mixed peel
- 1/4 cup apple concentrate (or as required)
- zest of 1 lime
- 1/2 cup sultanas
- 1/2 cup currants

Soy ice-cream

- 1/4 cup honey (or as required)
- 100 ml water
- 1 litre low-fat soy milk
- 2 egg whites
- 1/2 cup mixed peel
- 1/2 cup sultanas
- 1/2 cup currants
- zest of 1 lime

Orange glaze sauce

- 1/2 cup apple concentrate
- zest of 1 orange
- 2 cups orange juice

Iced Christmas pudding

Place the softened (but not thawed) soy ice-cream in a mixing bowl and add all the remaining ingredients. Mix together until well combined. Spoon into a large pudding mould that has been lined with plastic food wrap. Cover and freeze until firm. Remove from the freezer 10 minutes before serving.

To make the soy ice-cream, place the water, lime zest and honey in a small saucepan. Bring to the boil and simmer for 1 minute. Cool. Meanwhile, place the milk in an ice-cream churn and churn until creamy. Lightly beat the egg whites and fold into the creamy mix together with the boiled lime zest and honey mix and continue to churn until frozen. Place in a bowl and mix in the fruits (this may also be done during the last 30 seconds of the churning, but care must be taken not to over-churn the mix or it will discolour).

To make the sauce, bring the orange juice, apple concentrate and orange zest to the boil. Simmer slowly until it has reduced by three-quarters and cool. Spoon around the pudding.

Sticky Date Pudding

Serves: 16 Calories: 125 Fat: 3.5 gm

- 170 gm dates
- 1 tsp baking soda
- 300 ml water, boiling
- 80 ml honey
- 60 gm unsalted butter
- 2 egg whites
- 90 gm wholegrain wheat flour
- 1 egg
- 90 gm all-purpose white wheat flour
- 1/2 tsp vanilla extract
- 1 tsp low-sodium baking powder

Pre-heat oven to 180C. Line a 20 cm round baking tin with greaseproof paper. Mix the dates and boiling water in a bowl and leave to stand for 10 minutes. Then add the bicarbonate of soda.

Meanwhile, in an electric blender, cream the butter and honey, then add the egg and the egg whites one at a time, taking care to mix each one in well before adding the next. Add the baking powder and flours and continue to mix slowly. Gently fold in the soaked dates and the vanilla extract. Pour the mixture into the prepared tin, bake in the centre of the pre-heated oven for about 30-40 minutes or until a skewer inserted into the centre of the pudding comes out clean. Best served with Honey and Ginger Ice-Cream (see page 126).

Sticky date pudding

Honey and ginger ice-cream

Honey and Ginger Ice-cream

Serves: 30 x 50 ml Calories: 25 Fat: 0.4 gm

- 20 gm ginger powder
- 100 ml water
- 1 litre low-fat soy milk
- 180 gm honey
- 2 egg whites

In a small saucepan, place the water, ginger and honey. Bring to the boil and simmer for 1 minute. Remove from the heat and leave to stand for 20 minutes to cool.

Meanwhile, place the milk in an ice-cream churn and churn until creamy. Lightly beat the egg whites and fold into the creamy mix together with the honey mix, and continue to churn until frozen.

Remove and place in an ice-cream storage container and put into a freezer for at least one hour to firm before serving.

To serve, use a 50 ml ice-cream scoop for the correct calorie count.

Chayanat's Pumpkin Delight

Serves: 35 Calories: 70 Fat: 3.0 gm

- 400 gm yellow pumpkin, peeled and cubed
- 1 cup rice flour
- 2 tbsp tapioca flour
- 200 gm fresh coconut, grated
- 1/4 tsp salt
- 100 gm fresh young coconut flesh
- 3/4 cup sugar
- 1/4 cup water
- 1 cup young coconut water

Steam the pumpkin until soft, then mash until nearly smooth. Add 1/4 cup warm water to the grated coconut and use the hands to squeeze 1 cup of coconut milk. Mix the pumpkin with the flours, salt, sugar and 50 gm fresh coconut flesh. Slowly blend in the coconut milk. Pour the mix into small metal jelly moulds, or a large, square baking dish.

Top with the remaining coconut and pat down lightly. Steam for 30 minutes until cooked. Cut when cold to serve.

Chayanat's pumpkin delight

Thai coconut brownie (babin)

Thai Coconut Brownie (Babin)

Makes: 60 Calories: 75 Fat: 1.9 gm

- 3 egg whites
- 125 gm rice flour
- 125 gm tapioca flour
- 2 cups sugar
- 300 gm fresh coconut flesh
- 250 ml coconut water
- 500 gm fresh coconut, grated

Beat the egg whites and sugar together but do not aerate them. Add the rice and tapioca flours. Mix well.

In a food processor, pulse blend the young coconut flesh and the coconut water together until creamy. Strain and reserve the liquid. Discard the coconut. Add the reserved liquid to the egg mix.

Meanwhile, toast the grated coconut in a warm oven until fragrant but not coloured. Allow to cool slightly. Combine the toasted coconut and the egg mix and mix well.

Pour into a shallow baking tray and bake at 200C for 20 minutes or until golden. Cool. Cut and serve.

Raspberry streusel

Bakery

Raspberry Streusel

Serves: 12 Calories: 150 Fat: 0.9 gm

- 2/3 cup skim milk
- 30 ml lemon juice
- 1 1/2 cup flour
- 1/2 cup oat flour
- 1/2 cup sugar
- 4 tsp baking powder
- 1 tbsp lemon zest
- 1 egg white
- 1 1/2 cups frozen raspberries

Topping

- 2/4 cup instant oats
- 1 tbsp wheat germ
- 2 tsp apple concentrate
- 1/6 tsp nutmeg

Mix the instant oats, wheat germ and nutmeg with apple concentrate and set aside. Mix the milk and lemon juice, and set aside. Combine the flours, sugar, baking powder and lemon zest. Stir in the egg white and frozen raspberries. Pour into a 20 cm tin. To make the topping, combine all the ingredients together and sprinkle on top of the strawberry mix. Bake at 180C for 35-40 minutes.

Dried Apple Cake

Makes: 16 slices Calories: 85 Fat: 3.4 gm

- 1/4 cup butter
- 1/3 cup sugar
- 1/4 tsp vanilla extract
- 1/2 tsp salt
- 1/2 tsp cinnamon, ground
- 1 egg
- 1/2 cup milk
- 1 cup rice flour
- 3/4 cup dried apples, chopped
- 1 tsp baking soda

Cream the butter and sugar until light and airy. Add the vanilla, salt, cinnamon and egg. Beat well to combine. Mix the baking soda and rice flour together and sift if necessary to remove any lumps of flour. Mix in the dried apples. Add the milk to the egg mixture, then fold in the apple and flour mix. Do not over-mix. Pour into a non-stick cake ring and bake at 160C for 20-25 minutes.

Banana Cake

Serves: 16 Calories: 95 Fat: 0.9 gm

- 2 eggs
- 1/3 cup raw sugar
- 4 medium bananas
- 1/2 tsp baking soda
- 1 1/4 cups brown rice flour
- 1/2 tsp baking powder

Beat the egg with the sugar for about 7-8 minutes until triple in volume. Mash the bananas and add the baking soda, then fold into the egg mix. Combine the rice flour with the baking powder and fold into the banana mix gently but quickly. Pour into a non-stick baking tin and bake at 160C for approximately 30 minutes, or until a skewer inserted into the middle comes out clean.

Dried apple cake

Banana cake (wheat-free)

Passion fruit rice cake

Tofu pie

Passion Fruit Rice Cake

Serves: 16 Calories: 115 Fat: 2.7 gm

- 1/4 cup unsalted butter
- 1/4 cup sugar
- 1 cup white rice flour
- 2 egg whites
- 2 tbsp passion fruit pulp, without liquid
- 1 tsp baking powder
- 1/3 cup tepid milk

Cream the butter and sugar together in a mixer, then slowly add the egg whites, being careful not to add it too fast or it will split the butter. Using a slower speed on the mixer, add the flour and baking powder then the milk and passion fruit. Combine well in the mixer, then pour into a 30 cm round non-stick cake tin. Bake for about 30 minutes at 170C. Place a skewer into the centre of the cake after 30 minutes and if you can remove it cleanly then the cake is done. Remove from the oven, and turn out onto a wire rack to cool. Serve with a fruit puree or herbal tea.

Tofu Pie

Serves: 12 Calories: 60 Fat: 2.1 gm

- 2 pieces firm tofu
- 2 1/2 tbsp honey
- 1/8 cup raisins
- 2 tsp lemon juice
- zest of 1 lemon
- 2 eggs

For the base

- 1/2 cup rolled oats
- 1/2 cup dried okara
- biscuit crumbs
- 2 tsp lemon juice
- 2 tsp honey
- 2 tsp butter

Pre-heat the oven to 170C. Beat the tofu in a mixer until smooth. Add the honey, lemon juice, lemon zest and eggs. Lastly fold in the raisins.

For the base, combine all the ingredients together in a bowl and mix with the fingertips until just combined. Press into a non-stick cake ring. Pour in the filling and bake for 20-25 minutes, or until firm. Cool completely before removing from the cake ring to cut and serve.

Serving suggestion: The orange sauce of the Iced Christmas Pudding (see page 124) is an excellent sauce to serve with this pie.

Pineapple Flan

Serves: 16 Calories: 100 Fat: 2.0 gm

For the pastry case

- 175 gm unsalted butter, cold
- 1/4 cup sugar
- 30 gm wholewheat flour
- 230 gm plain flour
- 30 gm egg white
- water as needed

For the filling

- 1 1/2 cups very ripe pineapple
- 1/4 cup sugar
- 1/4 cup raisins
- 1 tbsp cornstarch
- 1 tbsp water

For the crumb topping

- 30 gm butter, chilled
- 60 gm flour
- 15 gm sugar

With your fingertips, crumb the cold butter, flours and sugar together. When well combined, add the egg and water (as needed). Let the pastry rest in the fridge for about 1 hour, then roll out to about 1/2 cm thickness and line a 25 cm flan tin. Let it rest for another hour, then blind-bake at 175C until golden brown.

To make the filling, take the pineapple, chop into 1 cm x 1 cm pieces, place in a pot with the water and bring to the boil. Taste the pineapple liquid and adjust with the sugar if needed (for a very ripe pineapple, no sugar is necessary as it will be sweet). Mix the corn flour with the water and thicken the liquid until it thinly coats the back of a spoon, and set aside to cool.

To make the topping, use either your fingers or a blender. Add all the ingredients together and rub into crumbs, then set aside in a cool place.

Take the pastry case, fill it with the cool but still liquid filling, sprinkle the crumb mix over the top, then bake for 20 minutes in a moderate oven. Cool, then slice into 16 pieces and serve.

Passion Fruit Tart

Serves: 10 Calories: 170 Fat: 6.4 gm

- 300 ml orange juice
- 300 ml water
- 40 ml passion fruit pulp
- 35 gm cornstarch
- 1/4 cup honey
- 1/4 cup apple juice concentrate
- 1/6 wheat-free pastry

Wheat-free pastry

- 200 gm brown rice flour
- 500 gm light rye flour
- 1/2 tsp stevia green leaf powder*
- 200 gm soy flour
- 80 ml water (or as required)
- 400 gm unsalted butter

Roll out the pastry to approximately 2 mm thick and line individual tartlet moulds by lightly pressing the pastry in. Refrigerate for 1 hour. When well chilled, bake the tartlets in a moderate oven for 5-6 minutes or until golden. Cool.

Meanwhile combine the orange juice, water, honey and passion fruit pulp in a saucepan and bring to the boil. Mix the apple concentrate with the cornstarch and pour into the simmering orange mix. Continue to stir for 1-2 minutes after the mix thickens. Pour into the cooled pastry cases. Set aside in a cool place. Best served on the day of baking.

To make the wheat-free pastry, place the flours in an electric mixing bowl together with the stevia. Gently mix with the paddle blade. Add the butter and continue to mix on a slow speed until the butter is incorporated. Add sufficient water to combine all the ingredients into a ball. Remove from the machine. Wrap in plastic food wrap and place in a refrigerator to rest for 30 minutes before using.

** Stevia is a native shrub of Paraguay which has the sweetness of sugar but without the calories. It is available in liquid, refined powder or green leaf powder forms and has up to 400 times the sweetness of sugar by volume. For beginners, the green leaf powder is the easiest to use.*

Pineapple flan (page 133)

Passion fruit tart

Oat and walnut bread

Rye bread

Rye and flax seed bread

Oat and Walnut Bread

Serves: 20 rolls Calories: 64 Fat: 2.1 gm

- 500 gm oat flour
- 15 gm yeast
- 5 gm salt
- 10 gm sugar
- 20 gm walnuts, chopped
- 20 ml walnut oil
- 250 ml tepid water

Dissolve the yeast in the tepid water with the sugar. Leave in a warm place to double in volume. Combine the flour with the salt and walnuts (or other ingredients). Make a well in the centre. Pour in the oil and the dissolved yeast mixture and mix all together well. Knead until smooth and elastic. Cover with a cloth and set aside in a warm place for 30 minutes to 1 hour, or until double in volume. Knock back, divide into rolls and shape as required. Leave to prove (it will not double in size the same as traditional bread), then bake at 200C for 10-12 minutes, or until a golden colour.

This recipe does not contain the same gluten content as most breads, because it is wheat-free. Hence the bread will be in a heavy style. Care should be taken to not overcook it, and it should be eaten fresh. Do not store.

Rye Bread

Serves: 20 rolls Calories: 90 Fat: 2.2 gm

- 500 gm rye flour
- 15 gm yeast
- 5 gm salt
- 10 gm sugar
- 25 ml grapeseed oil
- 300 ml tepid water

Follow the instructions for the Oat and Walnut Bread.

Rye and Flax Seed Bread

Serves: 20 rolls Calories: 85 Fat: 2.0 gm

- 500 gm rye flour
- 15 gm yeast
- 5 gm salt
- 10 gm sugar
- 25 ml grapeseed oil
- 350 ml tepid water
- 50 gm flax seeds

Follow the instructions for the Oat and Walnut Bread.

Barley and sunflower seed bread

Buckwheat and corn bread

Barley and Sunflower Seed Bread

Serves: 16 Calories: 102 Fat: 2.4 gm

- 200 gm rye flour
- 300 gm barley flour
- 15 gm yeast
- 5 gm salt
- 10 gm sugar
- 25 ml grapeseed oil
- 50 gm sunflower seeds
- 250 ml tepid water

Follow the instructions for the Oat and Walnut Bread.

Buckwheat and Corn Bread

Serves: 10 Calories: 105 Fat: 2.1 gm

- 220 gm buckwheat
- 5 gm salt
- 10 gm baking powder
- 50 gm cornmeal
- 20 ml grapeseed oil
- 200 ml water

Follow the instructions for the Soy and Fennel Seed Bread.

Soy and Fennel Seed Bread

Serves: 10 rolls Calories: 85 Fat: 1.8 gm

- 250 gm soy flour
- 5 gm salt
- 10 gm baking powder
- 280 ml water
- 10 gm fennel seeds
- 20 ml grapeseed oil

Mix and aerate all the dry ingredients together. Add the water and oil and mix well. Place into a piping bag and pipe onto non-stick baking sheets. Bake at 180C for 15-20 minutes or until golden.

Soy and fennel seed bread

10
Miscellaneous

Chickpea butter

Cottage cheese

Chickpea Butter

Makes: 20 tbsp Calories: 40 Fat: 0.5 gm

- 250 gm dried chickpeas
- 2 tbsp honey
- 5 tsp cinnamon
- 10 ml vanilla extract
- water

Soak the chickpeas in water overnight. Cover the chickpeas with twice the amount of water and bring to the boil. Continue boiling until the peas are tender (approximately 20 minutes). Drain and place the chickpeas into a mincer fitted with a small blade. If a slightly crunchy consistency is desired, use a larger blade. After processing, add the other ingredients to the chickpea paste and mix well. You may need to add a little water if the paste is too dry.

Serve chilled with toast, crumpets, croissants or spread on bread as a sandwich. Keep in the refrigerator.

Cottage Cheese

Makes: 6 x 50 ml portions Calories: 20 Fat: 0.8 gm

- 1 litre low-fat milk
- half lemon, juice only

Bring the milk just to the boil. Add the lemon juice and remove from the heat. Cool slightly for 15-20 minutes. Bring back to the boil and let cool again. The milk will have curdled. Pour into a strainer lined with cheesecloth or similar. Take the corners of the cloth and tie together with a string, and suspend over a bowl for 1-2 hours to drain fully. Do not force the whey out of the curds as this will affect the texture. Chill and serve as required. The texture can be adjusted by leaving for a shorter time, or place the curds in a blender and blend to a smooth paste. If a creamier cheese is required, add a tablespoon of skim milk powder.

FSA

Garam masala

FSA (flax seed, sunflower seed, almond)

Serving: per teaspoon Calories: 45 Fat: 3.4 gm

- 1 tbsp flax seeds
- 1 tbsp almonds
- 1 tbsp sunflower seeds

Combine all the ingredients in a food processor and blend until almost smooth. Sprinkle on salads or breakfast cereals. A good source of essential fatty acids.

Garam Masala

Serves: Makes 48 x 2 gm portions Calories: 7 Fat: 0.3 gm

- 30 gm coriander seeds
- 30 gm cumin seeds
- 16 cm cinnamon sticks
- 1 1/2 cardamom pods
- 1 1/2 tsp whole cloves
- 4 bay laurel
- 3 tbsp black peppercorns
- 1/2 tsp ground mace (optional)

In a heavy-based pan, dry-fry all the spices until fragrant. Cool completely and place in a spice grinder to grind to a fine powder. It can be stored in an airtight container for up to 60 days.

Salt substitute

Tofu mayonnaise

Chiva-Som Salt Substitute

Serving: per teaspoon Calories: 8 Fat: 1 gm

- 1 tsp mace, ground
- 1 tsp onion powder
- 1 tsp black pepper, ground
- 1 tsp sage, ground
- 1 tsp dried marjoram
- 1 tsp basil, dried
- 1 tbs red or cayenne pepper
- 1 tsp thyme, dried
- 1 tbsp garlic powder
- 1 tsp parsley, dried

Mix all the ingredients together. It must be stored in an air-tight container.

Tofu Mayonnaise

Serves: 60 tsp Calories: 16 Fat: 0.7 gm

- 440 gm silken tofu
- 60 gm apple cider vinegar
- 3 tsp sesame seeds, roasted
- 20 gm yellow mustard

Remove the tofu from its packaging. Place all the ingredients into a blender and blend until smooth. Keep in a storage container.

Vegetable stock

Roasted garlic

Vegetable Stock

For 1 litre Calories: 100

- 2 tomatoes
- 1 Chinese celery
- 1/4 small cabbage (preferably Chinese cabbage)
- 1 medium brown onion with skin
- 1 medium carrot
- 1 litre water

Wash but do not peel the vegetables. Combine all together and simmer for 1 to 2 hours. Strain and discard the vegetables. Best when made fresh daily, but will keep for 2-3 days in the refrigerator. It can also be reduced by half and frozen to keep.

Roasted Garlic

Makes: 1 portion Calories: 40 Fat: 0

- 1 head garlic

Take a whole head of garlic, and without peeling it, steam for 30 minutes. Remove from the heat and place in a moderate oven at 180C for 10-15 minutes. The actual cooking time depends on the accuracy of the oven temperature. Care should be taken to avoid burning the garlic skin. Remove from the oven and allow to cool for 5 minutes. Cut off the head and serve. Alternatively, remove the soft flesh from its skin and blend slightly to serve as a spread.

Use as a replacement for butter.

Garlic vinaigrette

Green curry paste

Garlic Vinaigrette

Makes: 20 x 20 ml portions Calories: 21 Fat: 0.04 gm

- 3/4 cup apple juice concentrate
- 2 tbsp lemon juice
- 2 tsp lemon rind, grated
- 1/2 cup white wine vinegar
- 4 small cloves garlic, peeled and cut in half

Combine all the ingredients in a screw-top jar and keep in the refrigerator. Shake every now and then. Remove the garlic prior to serving, or remove and crush then return to the vinaigrette.

Green Curry Paste

Makes approximately 180 ml

- 3 bay leaves
- 3 tsp pepper
- 1 tsp coriander seeds
- 1/2 cup green chilli
- 6 cloves garlic
- 1 tsp cumin
- 1 tbsp ginger, grated
- 2 green onions
- 1/2 lime

Soak the coriander seeds in a little boiling water until they soften slightly. Add the soaked seeds to the remaining ingredients and place in a food processor, or pound in a mortar. If it is too dry, add a little of the soaking water. Store in an airtight container.

Red curry paste

Red lentils with spices

Red Curry Paste

Makes approximately 180 ml

- 12 dried red chillies
- 1 tbsp lemon grass
- 1 tbsp galangal or ginger
- 6 shallots
- 2 tsp coriander seeds
- 6 cloves garlic
- 1 tsp caraway seeds
- 1 tsp shrimp paste
- 4 kaffir lime leaves

Soak the seeds in a little boiling water until they soften slightly. Add the soaked seeds to the remaining ingredients and place in a food processor, or pound in a mortar. If it is too dry, add a little of the soaking water. Store in an airtight container.

Red Lentils with Spices

Serves: 8 appetisers Calories: 135 Fat: 0.5 gm

- 250 gm red lentils
- 1/2 tsp turmeric, ground
- 125 ml vegetable stock
- 2 onions, finely diced
- 6 red tomatoes, finely chopped
- 1/2 tsp mustard seeds
- 1/2 tsp black onion seeds
- 125 ml vegetable stock
- 6 green chillies
- 1 litre water
- 1 tsp salt
- 1 tbsp ginger, grated
- 1/2 tsp cumin seeds
- 1/2 tsp fennel seeds
- 1/2 tsp fenugreek seeds

In a saucepan place the lentils, chillies, turmeric and water. Cook over a medium heat for 40 minutes, stirring occasionally. Cover and on a low heat cook for a further 5-10 minutes until soft. Place 125 ml vegetable stock in another saucepan with the chopped onions, and cook until soft. Add the tomatoes and ginger, and cook down to a paste. Fold into the cooked lentils and simmer a further 5-10 minutes until the flavours have blended. Set aside in a warm place.

In a third saucepan, place 125 ml vegetable stock together with cumin, fennel, mustard, fenugreek and black onion seeds, and cook until dry and fragrant. Add the bay leaves, dried chillies and garlic, and mix well. Dry-fry without burning the garlic. Add a little extra stock to moisten and pour over the lentil mix. Serve with crisp bread and a salad for a healthy snack or a light lunch.

LIST OF

BREAKFAST

APPETISERS

SOUPS

SALADS

FISH

MEAT

RECIPES

VEGETABLES

DESSERTS

BAKERY

MISCELLANEOUS